PLANET EARTH DATA RESOURCES

HARPER'S GEOSCIENCE SERIES
CAREY CRONEIS, EDITOR

Planet Earth Data Resources

Supplement to
Planet Earth: Its Physical Systems Through Geologic Time

Arthur N. Strahler

Harper & Row, Publishers
New York · Evanston · San Francisco · London

PLANET EARTH DATA RESOURCES

Standard Book Number: 06-046458-5

Library of Congress Catalog Card Number: 71-186222

CONTENTS

Preface   vii

BANK 1.   **Earth Coordinates and Earth-Sun Relationships   1**
A. The Earth-Grid; Latitude and Longitude   1
B. Projections of the Earth-Grid   3
C. Earth's Orbit, Revolution, and Year   6
D. Seasons: Solstice and Equinox   8

BANK 2.   **Earth Magnetism   11**
A. Elements of the Earth's Magnetic Field   11
B. Measurement of Magnetic Elements   11
C. Isogonic Map of the United States   13

BANK 3.   **Earth's Figure and Gravity   14**
A. Earth Ellipsoids   14
B. Nautical Mile, Meter, Statute Mile   15
C. Gravity and Gravity Corrections   15
D. Earth's Mass and Density   18

BANK 4.   **Atmospheric Temperature, Pressure, and Winds; Ocean Currents   20**
A. Measurement of Radiation   20
B. Measurement of Atmospheric Temperature   20
C. Measurement of Barometric Pressure   22
D. Measurement of Winds   23
E. World Maps of Sea-Surface Temperatures   24
F. World Maps of Air Temperatures   25
G. World Maps of Barometric Pressures and Winds   27
H. World Ocean Currents   27

BANK 5.   **Atmospheric Moisture and Cyclonic Storms   34**
A. Measurement of Relative Humidity   34
B. Cloud Families and Types   34
C. Measurement of Precipitation   37
D. World Precipitation Types   38
E. Cyclonic Storm on the Surface Map   40
F. Cyclone Development under an Upper-Air Wave   41

BANK 6.   **Stream Systems   46**
A. Stream Gauging   46
B. Relation of Stream Velocity to Depth and Slope   47
C. Geometrical Laws of Stream Networks and Drainage Basins   48
D. Stream Discharge and Basin Area   52
E. Drainage Density   52

BANK 7.   **Silicate Minerals and Igneous Rocks   55**
           A. Chemical Grouping of Minerals   55
           B. Physical Properties of Minerals   55
           C. Silicate Minerals   57
           D. Atomic Structure of Crystalline Minerals   60
           E. Igneous Rock Textures   66
           F. The Granite-Gabbro Series   67
           G. Forms of Intrusive Rock Bodies   68

BANK 8.   **Minerals Found in Sediments   69**
           A. Alteration Products of Silicate Minerals   69
           B. The Heavy Detrital Minerals   71
           C. The Wentworth Scale of Size Grades   71
           D. Hydrogenic and Biogenic Minerals   71
           E. Properties of Representative Ore Minerals   74

BANK 9.   **Topographic and Geologic Maps   77**
           A. Contour Maps and Other Isopleth Maps   77
           B. Map Scale   78
           C. Geologic Maps and Structure Sections   80

BANK 10.   **Seismographs and Seismic Waves   82**
           A. Seismographs   82
           B. Interpreting the Seismogram   84
           C. Nature of Earthquake Waves   85
           D. Seismic Waves and the Earth's Core and Mantle   86
           E. Seismic Waves and Crustal Structure   88

BANK 13.   **Biostratigraphy and Evolution   90**
           A. Biostratigraphic Units   90
           B. Stratigraphic Columns and Their Correlation   90
           C. Time Units and Lithofacies   92
           D. Evolutionary Charts of Plants and Animals   94

BANK 14.   **North America in the Cenozoic Era   98**
           A. Evolution of the Appalachian Landscape   98
           B. North America in Cretaceous Time   98
           C. Radiocarbon Age Determination   101
           D. Wisconsinan Stage in the Middle West   102
           E. History of the Great Lakes   104
           F. Crustal Rise Following Unloading   107

BANK 15.   **The Celestial Sphere   108**
           A. Celestial Coordinates   108
           B. Celestial Globes and Maps   109
           C. Horizon System of Celestial Coordinates   111
           D. Sidereal Time   112

           Index   114

PREFACE

This volume consists of thirteen *data banks*, each relating to the textbook chapter of the same number in *Planet Earth: Its Physical Systems Through Geologic Time* (Harper & Row, Publishers, 1972). (There are no banks for Chapters 11 and 12.) These banks provide an enrichment of concepts covered in the textbook chapters; they can do much to fill in the framework of dynamic systems with information on the nature and classification of the structures and substances that are products of those systems.

The data banks also explain much about the tools of scientific investigation and how they are used to measure the fluxes of energy and matter of the various planetary systems. Those who want to make field and laboratory observations in various areas of the earth sciences—astronomy, meteorology, hydrology, mineralogy, petrology, stratigraphy, glacial geology, and others—will find the data banks particularly useful.

Arthur N. Strahler

BANK 1
EARTH COORDINATES AND
EARTH-SUN RELATIONSHIPS

A. THE EARTH-GRID; LATITUDE AND LONGITUDE

The *earth-grid* consists of a network of east-west lines, the *parallels of latitude,* and north-south lines, the *meridians of longitude* (Figure 1.1).

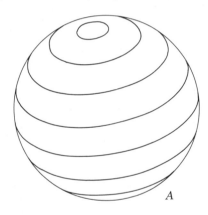

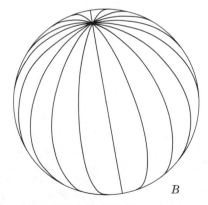

Figure 1.1. (*A*) Parallels. (*B*) Meridians.

The grid makes use of two types of circles. If a sphere is cut exactly in half by a plane passed through its center, the surface intersection of the plane defines a *great circle* (Figure 1.2), the largest possible circle that can be inscribed on a given sphere. Should a plane be passed through

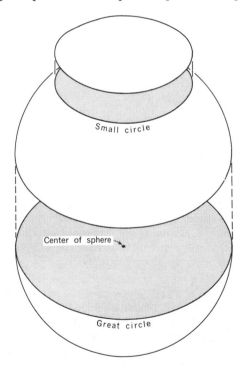

Figure 1.2. A great circle and a small circle.

a sphere in such a way that it does not pass through the center, the surface intersection is a *small circle.* Small circles can range in size from extremely tiny circles, approaching a point in smallness, to very large ones, which approach the diameter of a great circle, depending upon how near to the center the intersecting plane cuts through the sphere.

Great circles are needed in the earth sciences to plot the direction of surface travel of various kinds of waves generated from a point, to form hemispheres of darkness and light, or to find the opposite point, or *antipode,* with respect to any given point.

To find approximate great-circle arcs on a globe, stretch a string between the points, allowing the string to slip freely to a position such that its length is the shortest possible.

Rotation on an axis provides the earth with two fixed points of reference, the *geographic poles*, representing the points where the axis intersects the spherical surface (Figure 1.3). The

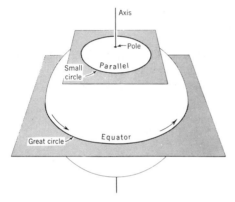

Figure 1.3. The equator and all other parallels lie in planes oriented at right angles to the earth's axis of rotation.

one great circle lying in a plane perpendicular to the axis midway between the poles defines the *equator* (which is the longest of the parallels). Small circles, possible in infinite number, can be formed by passing planes through the earth in positions parallel with the equator, thus producing all other parallels of latitude.

Parallels are all true east-west lines. In the earth-grid *east* and *west* are defined as the directions taken by the parallel passing through any given point. Every parallel is parallel to every other parallel; therefore the distance separating any two parallels remains constant. Parallels are infinite in number, and it is possible to pass a parallel through any desired surface point on the globe.

The earth's axis and poles also provide the reference points for defining meridians, which are halves of great circles, produced by passing planes through both poles simultaneously (Figure 1.4). Of course, the earth's axis also lies in the plane of a meridian. For each meridian there is a corresponding opposite meridian; the pair together constitute a full great circle. An individual meridian comprises 180° of arc, a half-circle; whereas a parallel comprises 360° of arc, a full circle.

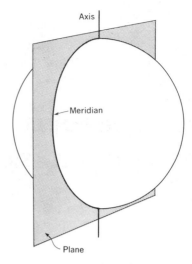

Figure 1.4. A plane passed through the earth's axis forms a meridian.

Because all meridians end at the poles, any two meridians are farthest apart at the equator, but converge poleward (Figure 1.1). Therefore the actual surface distance separating any two meridians decreases poleward, but the angular distance, or arc, between two meridians remains constant at all points because this is the angle formed by the intersection of the two planes which form the two meridians.

Meridians are true north-south lines. *Geographic north* is defined as the direction taken by a meridian through a given point, aiming in the direction of the north pole.

By measuring the arcs, or angular distances, along meridians and parallels with respect to one parallel and one meridian selected as the basic lines of reference, the location of any point on the globe can be uniquely stated in terms of the *geographic coordinates*: latitude and longitude.

The *latitude* of a place can be defined as the length of the arc of a meridian lying between that place and the equator (Figure 1.5). Latitude is stated in units of degrees and ranges from 0° at the equator to 90° N at the north pole (to 90° S at the south pole). Thus all latitude in the Northern Hemisphere must be designated as "north latitude" to distinguish it from the numerically equivalent "south latitude" of the Southern Hemisphere. Altogether, then, on the entire globe there are 180° of latitude.

The *longitude* of a place may be defined as the length of the arc of a parallel between that place and the *prime meridian*, a meridian arbitrarily accepted as the reference line (Figure 1.5). The prime meridian is given the longitude of 0°.

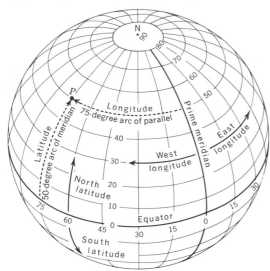

Figure 1.5. The geographic grid of parallels and meridians. Point *P* has a latitude of 50° N and a longitude of 75° W.

Longitude is measured eastward and westward from the prime meridian to a maximum value of 180° at the meridian that lies opposite the prime meridian. Longitude measured eastward is described as "east longitude" to distinguish it from "west longitude," measured westward from the prime meridian. Thus the total number of degrees of longitude over the entire globe is 360, or twice as many as the total degrees of latitude.

The prime meridian in world-wide use today is the *meridian of Greenwich*, chosen as that meridian passing through the former location of the Royal Observatory at Greenwich, near London, England.

When the location of a point on the earth's surface is given in terms of latitude and longitude, the coordinates may be written:

lat. 34°12′31″ N, long. 77°03′41″ W

This may be read "latitude 34 degrees, 12 minutes, 31 seconds north, longitude 77 degrees, 3 minutes, 41 seconds west." Because of the awkwardness of calculating with minutes and seconds of arc, it is now common practice to state latitude and longitude in terms of the decimal parts of the degree. The above coordinates would thus become:

lat. 34.2086° N, long. 77.0614° W

B. PROJECTIONS OF THE EARTH-GRID

Data of the earth sciences must often be plotted and displayed on a world map. But the earth-grid of parallels and meridians is a spherical net and cannot be drawn on a flat sheet of paper

without serious distortion resulting. The earth-grid as it is shown on a plane represents a *map projection*. Many forms of projections exist; each has a special property of value, and each has a serious defect.

When a scientist is faced with the problem of selecting a map projection upon which to depict his data, he has before him two basic choices: (1) a *conformal* projection, on which the shape of any small area is correctly shown, or (2) an *equal-area* projection, on which a constant scale of areas is preserved over the entire map. The conformal projection always shows a right-angle (orthogonal) intersection of any parallel with any meridian, just as holds true for all corresponding intersections of parallels and meridians on the globe. On an equal-area projection a small square or circle, representing a given number of square miles, may be moved about over the map and will delimit the same area of ground surface wherever it is placed.

It is impossible to devise a map projection that is both conformal and equal-area. All conformal projections suffer from severe scale changes so that areas are not correctly represented. All equal-area projections suffer from serious distortions of shapes. Therefore a scientist wishing to depict the areal extent of some surface property (such as relative areas of oceans and continents) will select an equal-area projection, while a scientist wishing to show the configuration of a given linear property (such as isobars or weather fronts on a weather map) will choose a conformal projection. Most of the world maps shown in illustrations in the parent textbook, *Planet Earth: Its Physical Systems Through Geologic Time* (referred to subsequently in this volume as *Planet Earth*), are of four types: two are conformal; two are equal area.

Among the most important projections for scientific uses is the *stereographic projection*, a perfect conformal network (Figure 1.6). In concept, the intersections of meridians and parallels are projected upon a tangent plane from a point source lying diametrically opposite to the point of tangency, as shown in the construction diagram. Any point of tangency may be selected. *Polar projections* result when either pole is selected as the point of tangency, and *equatorial projections* when a point on the equator is selected. An *oblique*, or *tilted*, *projection* results from selection of a point between equator and poles. All three positions are illustrated in Figure 1.6.

In the stereographic projections, all lines are either straight lines or arcs of circles. Any small

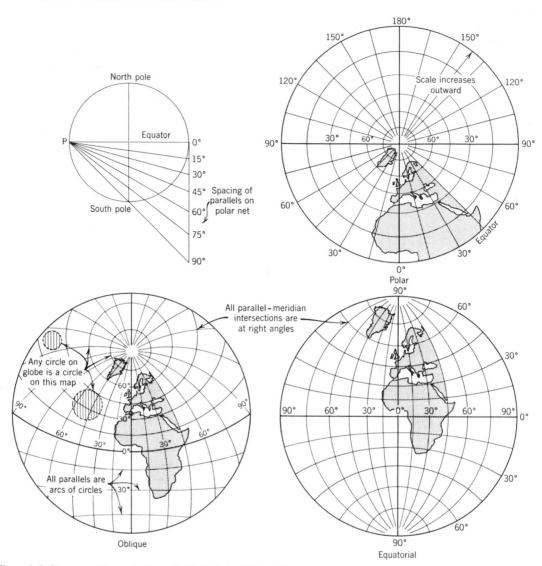

Figure 1.6. Stereographic projection. (© 1960, John Wiley & Sons, New York.)

circle on the globe is represented as a true circle on the projection. Map scale increases radially outward from the center of projection. It is impossible to show the entire globe on this projection.

The polar stereographic projection is generally selected for scientific maps of the polar regions. The National Weather Service of the National Oceanic and Atmospheric Administration (NOAA) uses a stereographic projection as the base for its surface-weather maps and upper-air charts. In seismology and geology, stereographic projections are useful to show the true patterns of island and mountain arcs and their associated earthquake epicenters. The stereographic network is also useful in the geometrical solution of problems in structural geology and in crystallography.

The *Mercator projection*, in its various forms, is perhaps the most useful of the true conformal projections for scientific purposes. In concept the network of parallels and meridians is drawn upon a cylinder enveloping the globe and tangent to it along a great circle. The cylinder is then imagined to be cut parallel to its axis and unrolled into a flat sheet. The Mercator projection thus has a single reference line—a great circle—along which the scale is constant. Scale increases away from this line in both directions.

The classic equatorial projection invented by Gerardus Mercator in 1569 is perhaps the best known of all map projections (Figure 1.7). Me-

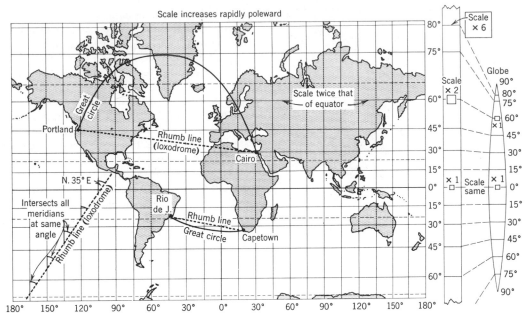

Figure 1.7. Equatorial Mercator projection. (© 1960, John Wiley & Sons, New York.)

ridians and parallels are straight lines forming a rectangular grid. Meridians are equidistantly spaced, while parallels are spaced at distances increasing rapidly away from the equator. To produce a true conformal projection, Mercator introduced exactly the right degree of north-south increase in scale needed to match the east-west increase in scale resulting from maintaining parallel meridians. Thus at 60° the east-west scale has been increased to twice that at the equator. (The 60th parallel of latitude is one-half as long as the equator.) Correspondingly, the north-south scale must be doubled. At 80° the scale increase is about sixfold. In mathematical terms, the scale on a Mercator projection increases poleward as the secant of the latitude. It is obvious that so rapid a scale increase makes it impractical to show regions poleward of, say, 85° and impossible to show the poles.

Although it is a true conformal projection depicting any small part of the earth's surface without shape distortion, the equatorial Mercator projection suffers from the vast increase in scale at high latitudes. Thus Greenland appears larger than South America, whereas it is actually only one-eighth as large.

A remarkable and unique quality of the equatorial Mercator projection is that any straight line drawn upon the map is a line of constant compass direction. Such a line is called a *rhumb line,* or *loxodrome* (Figure 1.7). Plotting of a rhumb line between any two points is, on the

Mercator projection, a simple matter of drawing a straight line connecting those points.

The Mercator projection is used in the earth sciences as a base for showing the world-wide variations of some physical property, such as magnetic declination (isogonic map), in which the azimuth of the lines is to be measured by protractor at various points. Another use is to plot the earth-track of satellites in oblique orbits. The Mercator projection is commonly misused, as when areal surface distributions are shown on it or when the geographic relations among points in the high latitudes are referred to it.

Equal-area projections are used to show the areal extent of some property of the earth's surface. For example, a world map of mean annual precipitation (Figure 5.7) uses an equal-area base map because emphasis is upon the quantity of area lying between successive isohyets or within a single closed isohyet, while on the other hand the compass direction taken by the isohyets is of only secondary importance, thus the map need not be conformal.

The *sinusoidal projection* is a true equal-area projection, making use of *sine curves* for meridians (Figure 1.8). Parallels are equidistantly spaced on this map, just as they are equally spaced on the globe. The sinusoidal projection can show the entire globe, but it suffers from extreme distortion of shapes in marginal zones at high latitudes.

The problem of marginal distortion can be

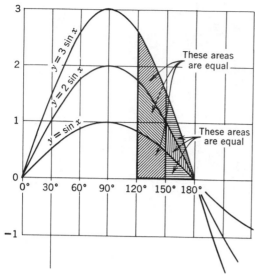

Figure 1.8. Sine curves as meridians in the sinusoidal projection. (© 1960, John Wiley & Sons, New York.)

largely solved by splitting apart the global network into sectors along certain meridians. The result is the *interrupted sinusoidal projection* shown in Figure 1.9. When the map is designed for showing continents to best advantage, interruption is made along meridians passing largely through oceans. Straight central meridians are chosen to be approximately centered upon each major landmass. Polar areas suffer badly from fragmentation, but low and middle latitudes have good continuity and excellent depiction of shapes.

For showing areal data of arctic and polar regions, the *azimuthal equal-area projection* is used (Figure 1.10). Examples are shown in the world temperature maps of Figures 4.15 and 4.16. In addition to being a true equal-area net, this projection has only minor shape distortion poleward of the 40th parallels. Map scale along the meridians decreases gradually from pole toward equator, whereas scale of the polar stereographic projection increases gradually in the same direction.

In summary, a good selection for conformal presentation is a Mercator projection combined with two polar stereographic projections, one for each polar region. A good selection for equal-area presentation is an interrupted sinusoidal projection combined with two pole-centered azimuthal equal-area projections.

C. EARTH'S ORBIT, REVOLUTION, AND YEAR

The earth travels in an elliptical orbit around the sun, which is situated at one *focus* of the ellipse (Figure 1.11). Earth motion in its orbit constitutes *revolution*; the period of revolution is the *year*. At its nearest point to the sun, *perihelion*, about January 3 of each year, the separating distance is about 91½ million miles (147×10^6 km); at its farthest point, *aphelion*, the distance is about 94½ million miles (152×10^6 km). Mean distance is about 93 million miles (150×10^6 km).

Average orbital velocity of the earth is about 66,600 mi (107,000 km) per hour, or about 18½

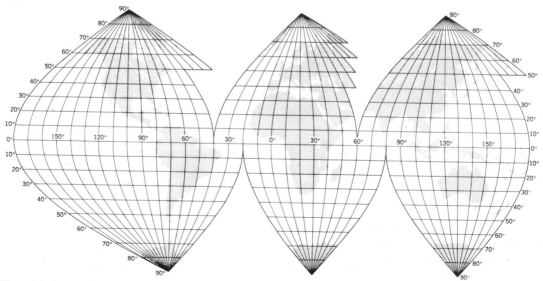

Figure 1.9. Interrupted sinusoidal projection, designed in 1970 by A. N. Strahler. Interruption of Eurasia on the 60th meridian east minimizes distortion in eastern Asia.

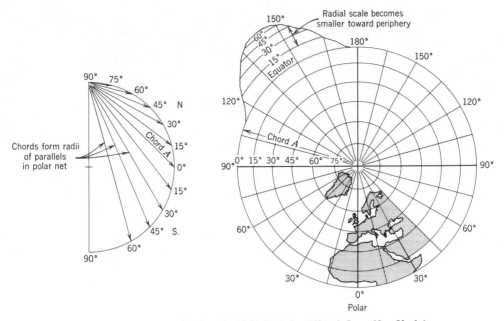

Figure 1.10. Polar azimuthal equal-area projection. (© 1960, by John Wiley & Sons, New York.)

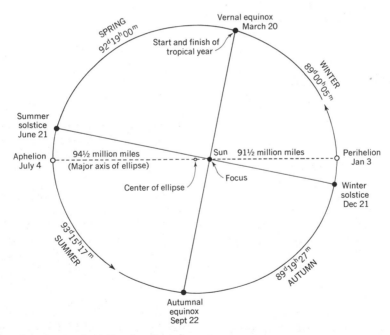

Figure 1.11. Dates of equinox and solstice; duration of seasons.

mi (29.6 km) per second. Velocity is greatest at perihelion, least at aphelion.

What is generally meant by the word *year*, particularly insofar as our calendar is concerned, is correctly termed the *tropical year*, defined as the time elapsed between two successive crossings by the sun of the celestial equator at the point known as the *vernal equinox*. The tropical year has a length of 365 days, 5 hr, 48 min, and 46 sec (written $365^d5^h48^m46^s$), or 365.242 days. The units are of *mean solar time*. Because our calendar year is one of exactly 365 days, there is an excess of almost 6 hr, or one-quarter of a day, per tropical year. By adding a day (February 29) each leap year, which comes every fourth year, this excess is largely corrected.

A second definition of a year is the time elapsed between successive occupations of exactly the same orbital point with reference to a given star. This is the *sidereal year,* with a value of $365^d6^h9^m10^s$ (365.256 days). The adjective "sidereal" simply means "referring to the stars." The sidereal year is thus about 20^m23^s (0.0142 day) longer than the tropical year.

We may note a third kind of year, the *anomalistic year,* defined as the time elapsed from one perihelion to the next; it is equal to $365^d6^h13^m53^s$ (365.260 days).

D. SEASONS: SOLSTICE AND EQUINOX

As rigorously defined in astronomy, the equinoxes and solstices are points on the ecliptic circle of the celestial sphere occupied by the sun when its declination is either zero (the *equinoxes*) or at the maximum value of 23½° N or S (the *solstices*). The equinoxes and solstices may also be defined as points in the earth's orbit (Figure 1.11). The major axis of the elliptical orbit defines the points of perhelion and aphelion, with the sun located at one focus. If a straight line is drawn from vernal equinox to autumnal equinox, as in Figure 1.11, the line will pass through the sun. Similarly a line connecting solstices will pass through the sun. Moreover these two straight lines will intersect at right angles.

The critical dates are: vernal equinox, March 20 or 21; summer solstice, June 21 or 22; autumnal equinox, September 22 or 23; winter solstice, December 21 or 22. The reason for giving alternate calendar dates for each is that the actual instant at which the earth is in a given equinox or solstice point ranges through 2 days because the tropical year is about a quarter of a day longer than a normal calendar year. Thus vernal equinox occurs $05^h48^m46^s$ later each year for 3 years, bringing it from March 20 into March 21, after which the added day in leap year restores the equinox to March 20.

From Figure 1.11, we see that the time intervals elapsing between one equinox and the next solstice, etc., are not the same. If the earth's orbit were a perfect circle, the tropical year would be divided into four equal parts, each of about $91^d07^h27^m12\frac{1}{5}^s$. In Figure 1.11 the orbit is shown as an ellipse, unequally divided by the line connecting the equinoxes. Consequently, the longer part of the orbit falls in the spring-summer half of the year. Not only does the earth have there a greater length of orbit to negotiate, but it travels more slowly in the region of aphelion than in the region of perihelion. Elapsed times for the four quarters reflect this effect

quite nicely. The quarter from winter solstice to vernal equinox is the shortest of all, 89 days, because this quarter contains perihelion and the average orbital velocity of earth is greatest. The longest quarter, over 93½ days, is from summer solstice to autumnal equinox, because this period contains aphelion and hence the lowest average earth velocity.

Conditions on the dates of equinoxes can be analyzed by means of a meridional cross section of the earth (Figure 1.12). The earth's axis in this diagram appears to have no inclination; this is because the observer is imagined to have his eye in the plane of the equator so that his line of sight is inclined 23½° from the plane of the ecliptic. The sun's rays can be drawn as parallel lines tangent to the poles. The circle of illumination on this date passes through the poles and therefore coincides with the terrestrial meridians as the earth rotates.

Along a meridian coinciding with the illumination circle in one hemisphere, the sunrise is occurring for all points on the meridian; whereas the opposing meridian, 180° distant, is experiencing sunset. Solar noon in Figure 1.12 is occurring along the terrestrial meridian that at any given moment coincides with the right-hand edge of the earth's cross section; midnight is represented by the left-hand edge. At each of several latitudes in Figure 1.12 a short segment of straight line was drawn tangent to the globe to represent the horizon planes of observers at each point. The angle between the sun's rays and the tangent horizon plane is therefore the *altitude of the noon sun,* its angular distance above the horizon.

In Figure 1.12 we see that at the equator the sun's noon altitude is 90°, meaning that the noon sun occupies the zenith position. At the north pole, latitude 90° N, the sun at noon is exactly on the horizon and it must keep this position throughout the day as the earth rotates.

From geometrical relations between latitude and the sun's altitude, the following rule applies to the equinoxes: The altitude of the noon sun on the equinox date is equal to the *colatitude,* equivalent to 90° minus the latitude. For points having the same latitude in the Northern and Southern Hemispheres, the noon altitude is the same, except that it is measured above the south horizon point in the Northern Hemisphere and above the north horizon point in the Southern Hemisphere.

At equinox the circle of illumination exactly divides all parallels of latitude into halves. This means that any point on the rotating earth ex-

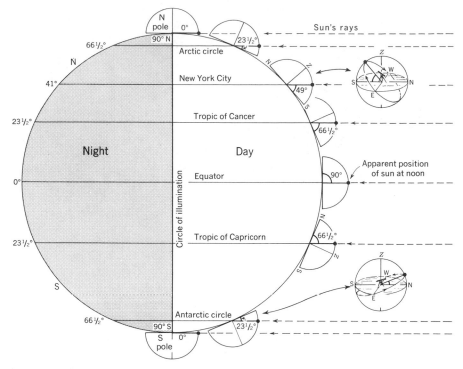

Figure 1.12. Altitude of the noon sun at equinox.

cept the poles will lie for 12 hr on the sunlit side of the globe and for 12 hr on the darkened side, hence that day and night are of equal length—12 hr each—over the entire globe. (For convenience the word "day" is used here to mean the period of time in which the sun is above the horizon.) For all latitudes except the poles, sunrise will occur at 6:00 A.M. (local apparent solar time) and will set at 6:00 P.M.

At winter solstice, December 22 or 23, the north polar end of the earth's axis is inclined the full $23\frac{1}{2}°$ away from the sun (Figure 1.13). Our viewpoint in Figure 1.14 is from the plane of the ecliptic opposed to the direction of the earth's orbital motion, with the sun to the right. The circle of illumination is tangent to the Arctic and Antarctic Circles, $66\frac{1}{2}°$ N and S, respectively, but still bisects the equator. The circle of illumination cuts the parallels of latitude into unequal parts. From this inequality it follows that the lengths of day and night will be unequal, except at the equator, and that the disparity increases from the equator poleward until, beyond the Arctic and Antarctic Circles, the day or night will last the full 24 hr.

Altitude of the noon sun at winter solstice is given in Figure 1.14 for various latitudes. At latitude $23\frac{1}{2}°$ S the sun's noon rays strike the earth perpendicularly, with the sun in the zenith

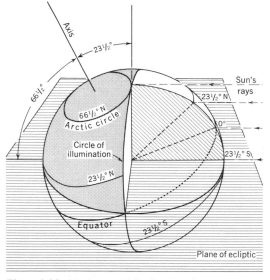

Figure 1.13. At winter solstice the sun's rays at noon are perpendicular at latitude $23\frac{1}{2}°$ S, the Tropic of Capricorn. All the region lying poleward of the Arctic Circle experiences night for the full 24 hr.

position. Consequently this parallel of latitude has a unique designation: the *Tropic of Capricorn*.

Further examination of Figure 1.14 shows that the sun's noon altitude at the equator is

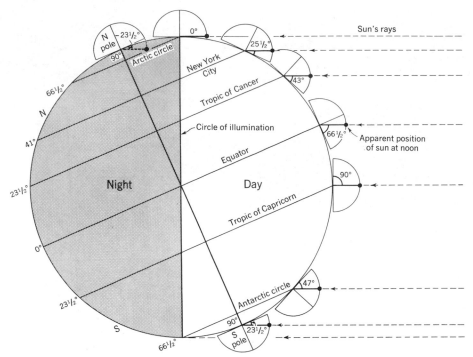

Figure 1.14. Altitude of the noon sun at winter solstice.

66½°; at latitude 41° N, 25½°; at 66½° N, 0°; at 66½° S, 47°; at the south pole, 23½°. A study of these numerical relations would reveal that the following rule applies: The sun's noon altitude at a given place is equal to 90° minus the arc of meridian between that place and the parallel over which the sun reaches zenith at noon. The rule applies equally well to any date of the year.

To study earth-sun relations at summer solstice, June 21 or 22, the same diagram in Figure 1.14 can be used by merely turning it upside down and changing "north" to read "south" and vice versa. All that has been said concerning winter-solstice conditions will apply if appropriate reversals are made in directions and hemispheres. An additional change will be to substitute *Tropic of Cancer* for Tropic of Capricorn, because at summer solstice the sun's declination is 23½° N and its noon rays strike the earth perpendicularly on the Tropic of Cancer, latitude 23½° N.

BANK 2
EARTH MAGNETISM

A. ELEMENTS OF THE EARTH'S MAGNETIC FIELD

The magnetic field at the earth's surface is completely described by three quantities, known as the *magnetic elements*—inclination, declination, and intensity. Of these elements, inclination and declination are angular quantities, stated in degrees, whereas intensity is a *vector quantity* (a force) requiring definition in terms of both direction and amount. Figure 2.1 shows the complete set of geometrical relationships among the magnetic elements. Space coordinates of the diagram consist of an X-axis directed toward geographic north, a Y-axis directed toward geographic east, and a Z-axis directed downward to the astronomical nadir. In this diagram, *total intensity* is represented by the arrow F and lies parallel to the lines of magnetic force. *Vertical intensity* is shown by the vertical arrow Z, *horizontal intensity* by the horizontal arrow H.

For detailed magnetic intensity maps, such as those of the United States issued by the NOAA National Ocean Survey, magnetic intensity is given in units of *gammas*. One oersted equals 100,000 gammas. Three intensity charts are available: Nos. 3077f, total intensity; 3077h, horizontal intensity; 3077z, vertical intensity.

B. MEASUREMENT OF MAGNETIC ELEMENTS

Precise measurements of the direction and intensity of the magnetic field are made continuously at some 90 permanent magnetic observatories distributed widely, but not uniformly, over the earth. In addition many observations are made by field parties to fill in necessary data for areas between permanent stations.

Among the magnetic properties measured are the inclination and declination, the total field intensity, the intensity in the horizontal and vertical directions, and the intensity in the north-south and east-west directions.

In general, an instrument that measures the intensity of the earth's magnetic field is called a *magnetometer*. One basic type is the *oscillation magnetometer*, which uses a bar magnet suspended in a horizontal attitude by a thread or mounted as a dip needle is. The magnet is set in rotary oscillation and the period of oscillation is measured, from which the horizontal or vertical components of field intensity can be calculated. The *deflection magnetometer* has a small fixed

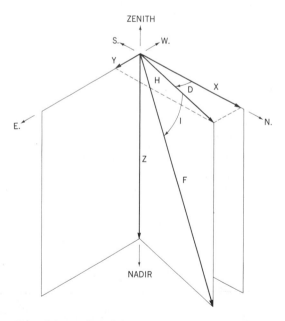

Figure 2.1. Vectors of the magnetic elements, as if seen from the northeast: D, declination; I, inclination, or dip; H, horizontal intensity; X, north component; Y, east component; Z, vertical intensity; F, total intensity. [From NOAA National Ocean Survey (1962), *Magnetism of the Earth*, Publ. 40-1, p. 6, Figure 1.]

magnet mounted near a magnetized compass needle, and the earth's field intensity is compared with the known field of the fixed magnet. A related instrument, using a Helmholz coil in place of the fixed magnet, is the *sine galvanometer.* This instrument has been used in magnetic observatories to measure the horizontal component of the earth's field.

A newer instrument yielding a much higher order of accuracy is the *proton vector magnetometer,* which makes use of the principle of precession of spinning protons set in motion by a

polarizing magnetic field. A central container of water provides the protons. Output from surrounding sensing coils is fed into automatic data-processing equipment for evaluation.

Portable magnetometers have been developed for outdoor use to make detailed maps of the field intensity and thereby to make inferences concerning the presence and outlines of rock bodies beneath the surface. The *airborne magnetometer,* an instrument carried by airplane, is capable of giving a continuous reading of the intensity as it is towed behind the plane along a

Figure 2.2. A typical magnetograph assembly at the Fredericksburg Geomagnetic Center. Instrument at right measures the *Z* element; that in center, the *D* element; that at left, the *H* element. (Refer to Figure 2.1.) Recorder is at far left. (NOAA National Ocean Survey photograph.)

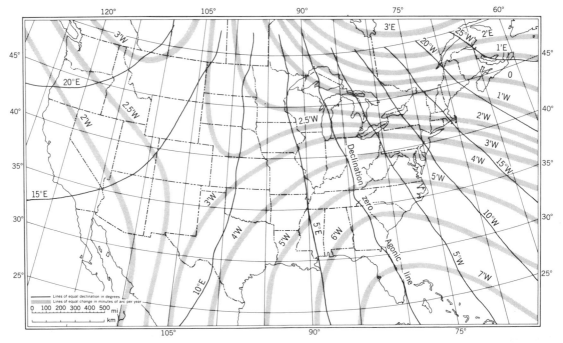

Figure 2.3. Isogonic map of the United States for 1965. (NOAA National Ocean Survey.)

line of traverse. The magnetometer may also be towed behind a ship to yield magnetic data over the ocean basins.

Magnetic fluctuations are monitored continuously at magnetic observatories, such as that located at Fredericksburg, Virginia, operated by the NOAA National Ocean Survey. Figure 2.2 shows a typical assemblage of observatory instruments, constituting a *magnetograph.* These use extremely sensitive magnets suspended or balanced in such a way as to respond to very rapid, slight changes in direction and intensity of the magnetic field. The magnetograph simultaneously records fluctuations in declination, horizontal intensity, and vertical intensity. The resulting record comprises a *magnetogram,* an example of which is given in *Planet Earth* Figure 2.2, showing the fluctuations in the *H, Z,* and

D elements of magnetic field intensity and in declination.

C. ISOGONIC MAP OF THE UNITED STATES

Figure 2.3 is an isogonic map of the United States showing declination of the compass for 1965. The *agonic line* (line of zero declination) runs through the Great Lakes and Florida. Superimposed as shaded bands are lines of equal annual change in declination. When this map is used to estimate the declination at a given location, the annual change multiplied by the number of years elapsed since preparation of the map (1965) should be added to or subtracted from the declination shown.

BANK 3
EARTH'S FIGURE AND GRAVITY

A. EARTH ELLIPSOIDS

Disregarding surface irregularities and secondary surface undulations due to place-to-place variations in mass of the earth's crust, the figure of the earth is best approximated by an oblate ellipsoid, which is an ellipse of revolution about its minor axis. The oblate ellipsoid has the form of an ellipse when cut through the plane of the poles (that is, in meridional cross section). The equatorial diameter forms the major axis of the ellipse, and the line of poles forms the minor axis (Figure 3.1). In equatorial cross section an

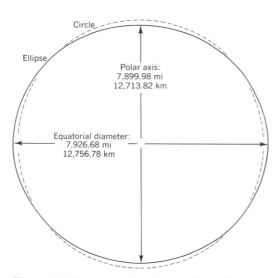

Figure 3.1. Dimensions of the International ellipsoid of reference.

oblate ellipsoid is a true circle, but the diameter of this circle is greater than the length of the polar axis, the difference being about 27 mi (17 km) as compared with an earth diameter of about 8000 mi (13,000 km).

Being a simple model and an idealized con-

cept, the earth ellipsoid has been assigned dimensions based upon the best geodetic information for the lengths of meridian arcs in various parts of the earth. Unfortunately, these measurements, precise as they may be, do not agree from one region to another for the earth's curvature at a given latitude. Consequently several geodesists have calculated what they believe to be the best earth ellipsoid. Selection of an ellipsoid for a particular area was made at a given time, in hopes that the ellipsoid dimensions would correspond to the geodetic data of that part of the world.

Earth ellipsoids are described in terms of the lengths of the *semimajor axis* (equatorial radius) and either the *semiminor axis* (one-half the polar axis) or the ratio of their difference to the semimajor axis, a constant known as the *flattening* (Figure 3.2). Flattening is quoted as a decimal number part or in fractional form. Table 3.1 gives the dimensions, in international meters, of

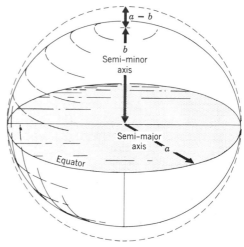

Figure 3.2. Semimajor and semiminor axes of the earth ellipsoid. (© 1960, John Wiley & Sons, New York.)

Table 3.1. DIMENSIONS OF SELECTED ELLIPSOIDS

Ellipsoid	Semimajor Axis[a] a	Semiminor Axis[a] b	Flattening f	Fractional Equivalent
International (Hayford, 1909)	6,378,388	6,356,912	0.003,367	1/297.00
Krasovskiy, 1942	6,378,245	6,356,863	0.003,352	1/298.3
Astrogeodetic, or Mercury Datum (Fischer, 1960)	6,378,160	6,356,778	0.003,352	1/298.3
Geodetic Reference System (IUGG, 1967)	6,378,160	6,356,775	0.003,353	1/298.25

[a]Measurements in international meters.

four ellipsoids that have been or presently are in wide use.

The *International ellipsoid* was computed by J. F. Hayford of the U.S. Coast and Geodetic Survey in 1909 and was adopted in 1924 by the International Union of Geodesy and Geophysics (IUGG) as a world standard. The *Krasovskiy ellipsoid* of 1942 is used by the U.S.S.R. and its satellite nations.

Major advances in calculation of the earth ellipsoid were made possible by the advent of orbiting earth satellites. Using earth-satellite data combined with all available geodetic data, a new ellipsoid was calculated in 1960 and named the *Astrogeodetic ellipsoid*. It was adopted for use by the Manned Space Flight Programs of NASA under the name of the *Mercury Datum*. The Fischer ellipsoid of 1960 uses a flattening of 1/298.3 and a semimajor axis of 6,378,160 m.

The International ellipsoid was replaced as a world standard in 1967, by action of the International Union of Geodesy and Geophysics, in favor of an ellipsoid designated as the *Geodetic Reference ellipsoid, 1967*. The semimajor axis of this ellipsoid is the same as that of the Astrogeodetic ellipsoid of 1960, but the reciprocal of the flattening is referred to more decimals: 1/298.25. These same dimensions had been adopted in 1964 by the International Astronomical Union.

On a perfect sphere, parallels of latitude spaced, say, $1°$ apart would be separated by exactly the same ground distance (1/360 of the earth's circumference) regardless of position on the globe. On an oblate ellipsoid, with its varying degree of meridian curvature from equator to pole, the length of $1°$ of latitude (a $1°$ arc of a meridian) increases systematically from equator to pole. The length of $1°$ of arc of the equator (a degree of longitude) would, on the other hand, be the same at all points around the earth, but this constant would differ slightly from the length of $1°$ of meridian arc (latitude) at the equator.

At the equator:

$1°$ of lat. = 68.7 mi (110.6 km)

At latitude $89°$ to $90°$ N or S:

$1°$ of lat. = 69.4 mi (111.7 km)

The difference between these two figures is about 0.7 mi (1.1 km), a large quantity to be reckoned with when precision is required in map making or when one's exact position must be located on the globe for navigation.

B. NAUTICAL MILE, METER, STATUTE MILE

For the purposes of marine and air navigation, as well as for many aspects of the earth sciences, the *nautical mile* is used as the unit of length or distance. Velocity of travel of aircraft and the speed of the upper-air currents are now given in terms of the *knot*, which is the mariner's traditional measure of speed, defined as 1 nautical mile per hour.

As a rough calculation, the nautical mile can be taken as the length of 1 minute of arc of a meridian, which is closely equivalent to 1.15 statute miles. The length of 60 nautical miles represents approximately the length of $1°$ of arc of a meridian and is roughly equivalent to 69 statute miles.

However, we have noted that the length of a degree of meridian arc varies from equator to pole, because of earth oblateness. The same statement also applies to the length of 1 minute of arc. To standardize the nautical mile, the entire length of a $90°$ arc of meridian between equator and pole is divided by the number of minutes, which is 5400, to give an average length for 1 minute of arc. Calculations will differ slightly depending upon the ellipsoid of reference selected. Consequently, an arbitrary value is used. In 1954 the U.S. Department of Defense adopted the *international nautical mile* as exactly equal to 1852 *international meters,* which comes very close to being equal to 6076.1 ft, or 1.1508 statute miles.

C. GRAVITY AND GRAVITY CORRECTIONS

Gravity is the force of gravitation exerted upon a unit of mass at or close to the earth's surface.

Gravity is defined as an *acceleration, g,* in terms of distance per unit of time per unit of time, representing the rate at which an object of any mass would increase its speed of fall at the earth's surface if dropped in a vacuum chamber. The value of g is approximately 32 ft/sec/sec (32 ft/sec^2) or 980 cm/sec/sec (980 cm/sec^2). Variations in the acceleration of gravity over the earth's surface result from three causes: (1) ellipsoidal form of the earth, (2) differences in elevation above or below sea level, and (3) differences in distribution of mass in the earth's crust and mantle.

Centripetal force of the earth's rotation reduces the earth's gravitational attraction by a small fraction, the effect being greatest at the equator and diminishing to zero at the poles (Figure 3.3). Gravity as actually measured

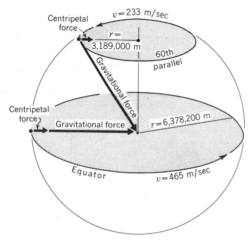

Figure 3.3. Centripetal force, which decreases as latitude increases, reduces very slightly the weight of an object on the earth's surface.

incorporates the effect of rotation. At the equator, the centripetal force due to rotation is 1/289 as great as the gravitational force. The fraction decreases poleward as follows:

Latitude	Fraction
0°	1/289
30°	1/385
45°	1/578
60°	1/1156

Assuming a spherical earth, the equation for computing the above fraction is:

$$\text{Fractional force} = \frac{1}{289} \cos^2 \text{lat.}$$

The precise value of the acceleration of gravity, g, is obtained by means of an extremely re-

fined and precise pendulum, using the principle that the period of swing of an ideal pendulum, T, depends solely upon two variable quantities: length of pendulum, L, and the acceleration of gravity, g. The basic equation for a simple pendulum is:

$$T = 2\pi \sqrt{\frac{L}{g}}$$

A world standard station for all gravity measurements was set up at Potsdam, Germany. There the value of 981.274 cm/sec^2 was determined for the acceleration of gravity by the pendulum method. The unit of gravity, known as the *gal* (named for Galileo), is equal to 1 cm/sec^2. Because gravity differences over the earth's surface are comparatively minute, the thousandth part of a gal, termed the *milligal* (mgal), is used as the unit for stating differences in gravity measurements. Observations on the absolute determination of gravity have been completed at Washington, D.C., Teddington, England, and Ottawa, Canada. These observations show that the Potsdam value is too high by about 14 mgal, but the Potsdam standard continues in use.

For the rapid measurement of acceleration of gravity at many points in the course of field surveys, a portable instrument known as the *gravimeter* is used. The gravimeter has a spring balance as its basic mechanism (Figure 3.4). A weight is hung from a coiled spring, whose change in length is proportional to the change in acceleration of

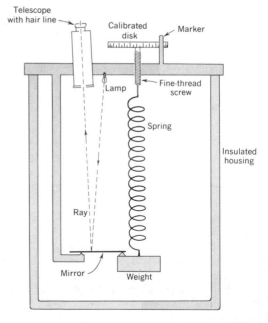

Figure 3.4. Simplified schematic diagram of a spring gravimeter.

gravity. Slight changes in spring length are amplified by a combination of mechanical, optical, and electrical means. The gravimeter must be calibrated against a series of base stations so that the differences in spring length can be interpreted as gravity values.

Suppose that a portable gravimeter has been calibrated at a series of base stations and has then been taken to a distant field location, perhaps in a mountainous region, where it has been set up. For what reasons might a single gravity reading differ from that of the base station?

Suppose first that the earth were of perfectly spherical outline and that the various types of materials composing it were formed into concentric, uniformly thick, spherical shells, arranged in order of decreasing density from the center outward. Under such conditions, gravity would be the same at all surface points, provided only that we have taken into account the effect of centripetal force of the earth's rotation varying with latitude. The question is then: In what ways can the conditions at our surface point of observation differ from such an ideal situation?

First, the earth approximates an oblate ellipsoid. Not only does this shape require a correction for the centripetal force distribution on the ellipsoid, but the greater mass lying nearer the equator must be taken into account. By use of the *international gravity formula of 1930* the expected normal gravity can be computed for any latitude. A value of 978.049 gal is assumed for the equator. The formula applies to the International ellipsoid (Hayford, 1909), for which the flattening ratio is exactly 1/297. Figure 3.5 shows

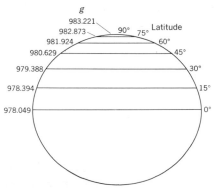

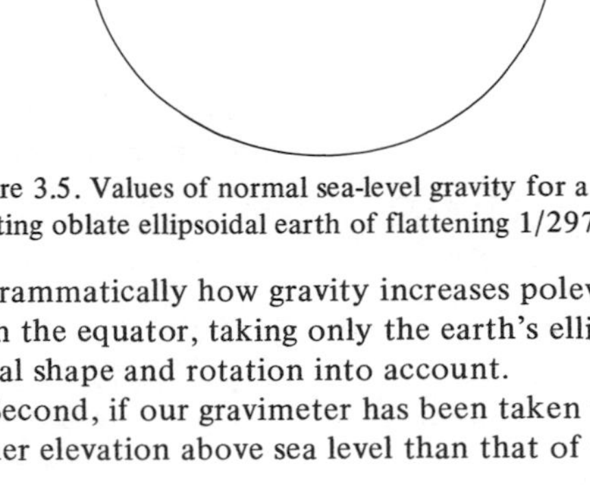

Figure 3.5. Values of normal sea-level gravity for a rotating oblate ellipsoidal earth of flattening 1/297.

diagrammatically how gravity increases poleward from the equator, taking only the earth's ellipsoidal shape and rotation into account.

Second, if our gravimeter has been taken to a higher elevation above sea level than that of the base station, it will register a lower value of gravity simply because it is farther from the earth's center. The correction of elevation, known as the *free-air correction,* can be obtained by solving a simple formula. As a rough approximation we can say that the value of gravity decreases about 1 mgal for 10 ft of ascent or about 1 mgal per 3 m (Figure 3.6).

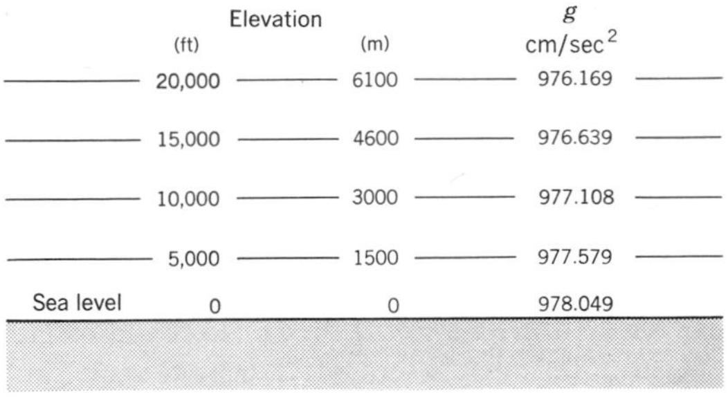

Elevation		g
(ft)	(m)	cm/sec^2
20,000	6100	976.169
15,000	4600	976.639
10,000	3000	977.108
5,000	1500	977.579
Sea level 0	0	978.049

Figure 3.6. Values of gravity with increasing elevation above the earth, based on sea-level value at equator.

A third correction to be made on our gravity reading is required by the earth's gross surface configuration. Where a high mountain or high plateau exists, a large mass of rock lies above sea level. This mass exerts a gravitational pull of its own. Therefore gravity at the imaginary ellipsoid surface will be somewhat less on high continental masses than it would be on a plain, all other conditions being the same.

The correction for effects of masses lying above the ellipsoid surface or for deficiencies of mass below that level is termed the *Bouguer correction.* This correction for mass distribution with respect to the ellipsoid surface is made with the assumption that the rock material has uniform density throughout, and hence that one need calculate only the volume of material between the earth's solid surface and the ellipsoid of reference. This assumption requires modification in view of geologic facts.

After applying the three classes of corrections thus far noted, plus a correction for the varying tidal pull of earth and sun, we may find that the observed value of gravity does not agree with the standard (Potsdam) value. A difference between observed and predicted gravity values is, in general, termed a *gravity anomaly.* When such an anomaly is found, a cause other than those already taken into account must be sought to explain the discrepancy.

The cause of such an anomaly, termed a *Bouguer anomaly,* lies in the different density of the great rock masses lying side by side in the earth's crust or mantle. In other words, the crustal or mantle rock under the station is actually denser or less dense than the assumed value. In Chapter 10 of *Planet Earth,* dealing with deformation of the earth's crust, the meaning of such anomalies is discussed.

D. EARTH'S MASS AND DENSITY

One clue to conditions within the earth is given by the astronomer, who has been able to measure the mass of the whole earth by use of Newton's laws of gravitation and mechanics. Mass is quantity of matter and is one of the fundamental properties of the physical universe. We cannot measure mass directly, but only through the force which it exerts owing to gravitational attraction.

Measurement of the earth's mass is relatively simple in principle, although precision determinations require elaborate precautions and refinements of the apparatus used. One simple approach we might consider is through the use of a pendulum of known mass. A second and larger known mass is brought close to one side of the pendulum mass. Mutual attraction between the two masses causes the pendulum mass to be moved slightly toward the larger mass (Figure 3.7*A*). The pendulum now assumes a position at rest, which is the resultant of the force of the earth's gravitational attraction and the force of attraction of the adjacent mass. The masses of earth and adjacent mass are thus in the same ratio as the two forces and could be calculated from measurements of the pendulum length and of the deflection of the pendulum mass. Unfortunately, the actual amount of pendulum deflection is so extremely minute as to be impossible to measure with the necessary degree of accuracy, so this method is not actually used.

One successful method of accurate determination of the earth's mass makes use of a beam balance of basically the same type used in laboratories for precision weighing, but much larger and sturdier in construction than the laboratory type (Figure 3.7*B*). The device is known as the *Poynting balance.* In the original experiment by Poynting, a mass, M_1, weighing 330 lb (136 kg) was placed on one pan and exactly counterbalanced by weights placed in the other pan. Then a much larger mass M_2, was placed under the pan containing the mass M_1, with their centers of mass separated by a distance D. Mutual attraction of the two masses pulled down their side of the balance, but this imbalance was corrected by the addition of small weights to the opposite pan until exact balance was again achieved. Thus a very small mass, m, counterbalanced the force of attraction between masses M_1 and M_2. Actually, it is the attraction between the earth, whose center is at distance R, and the small added mass, m, that exactly equals the mutual attraction of M_1 and M_2. Hence, using Newton's law of gravitation, we can write the equation:

$$G \frac{M_1 M_2}{D^2} = G \frac{M_e m}{R^2}$$

The symbol G stands for the *universal gravitational constant,* but since the two G terms cancel out, we need not know the value of G. All the other terms are known except the earth's mass, M_e; thus by solving for M_e, we obtain the desired answer. Recent precision determinations give the mass of the earth as about 6.6×10^{21} tons. A more nearly exact statement in metric units is 5.975×10^{27} gm.

Evaluation of the universal gravitational constant was made by Lord Cavendish in 1798, using a device known as the *torsion balance.* This evaluation enabled Cavendish to determine the mass of the earth. The torsion balance illustrated in Figure 3.7*C* consists of a delicate quartz fiber by which is suspended a balanced horizontal rod bearing a small sphere of platinum or gold at each end. From observations of the pendulum-like motion of the bar as it twists back and forth in a horizontal circle it is possible to calculate the force required to turn the bar through a given angular distance. Two large masses are then brought into place close to the two spheres and in the horizintal plane of their centers. Gravitational attraction between each sphere and the large mass adjacent to it causes the bar to be rotated by a very small amount from its initial position at rest. The magnitude of the attractional force can be calculated by the angle of deflection. The force of attraction is given by Newton's equation:

$$F = G \frac{M_1 M_2}{D^2}$$

Having measured the force, F, and knowing the masses, M_1 and M_2, and the separating distance, D, the value of G can be quickly calculated. When units of centimeters, grams, and seconds are used in the above equation, the value of G comes out to 6.66×10^{-8}. Using the known value of G, we can now calculate the earth's mass, M_e, from the equation:

$$M_e = \frac{gR^2}{G}$$

where g is the acceleration of gravity (980 cm/sec/sec) and R is the earth's radius (6.37×10^8 cm).

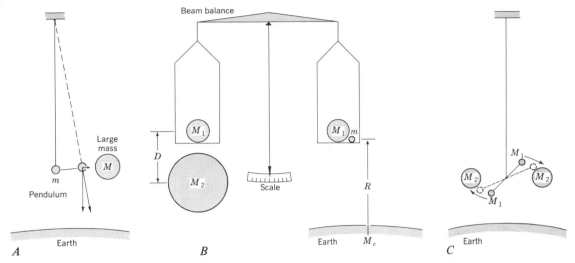

Figure 3.7. (*A*) A simple pendulum theoretically permits the earth's mass to be measured. (*B*) The Poynting balance is a practical instrument for determining the earth's mass. (*C*) The Cavendish torsion balance. [After T. G. Mehlin (1959), *Astronomy,* New York, Wiley.]

The resulting earth mass is the same as given for the beam balance determination, namely 5.975×10^{27} gm.

We can compute the volume of the earth from its ellipsoid dimensions, which comes out to 1.08×10^{27} cc. Dividing mass by volume yields the average density of the earth as 5.53 gm/cc. This figure is about twice the density of granite (2.6 gm/cc). Iron, in comparison, has a density of nearly 8 gm/cc.

The geophysicist reasons that because the greater part of known rock of the earth's outermost zone is of the density of granite (2.6 gm/cc) or of basalt (3.0 gm/cc), which are much less than the average figure of 5.53 gm/cc, density must increase greatly toward the earth's center. The most

reasonable conclusion is that there exists a core of high density, about 11.0 gm/cc. The core is usually considered to be composed largely of iron, because if iron were compressed in the earth's center under 2 to 3 million atmospheres of pressure, it would decrease in volume and thereby undergo a density increase from 8.0 to 11.0 gm/cc.

Between the outermost layer and the earth's core, density must range somewhere between 4.0 and 6.0 gm/cc. A rock that fits this requirement is dunite, an ultramafic rock composed largely of olivine (see Chapter 7 in *Planet Earth*). Its density is normally about 3.3 gm/cc, but would be increased to an acceptable value under the known confining pressures.

BANK 4

ATMOSPHERIC TEMPERATURE, PRESSURE, AND WINDS; OCEAN CURRENTS

A. MEASUREMENT OF RADIATION

Measurements of the incoming shortwave radiation are made continuously at a network of observing stations on the ground. Various types of instruments are available and perform a variety of functions. The *pyrheliometer* is a standard instrument for precision measurements; it is designed to measure the incoming radiation in a narrow beam directed at right angles to the receiving surface of the instrument.

An instrument used more widely is the *pyranometer*, which measures all shortwave radiation emanating within the 180° arc of the sky dome. It therefore senses both the direct solar beam and all incoming scattered radiation (Figure 4.1).

Figure 4.1. Pyranometer for measurement of solar and sky radiation. (Photograph by courtesy of Weather-Measure Corporation, Sacramento, Calif.)

The pyranometer can be exposed continuously at an observing station. About 75 stations using the pyranometer are in operation in the continental United States and form a network sufficiently dense to allow maps of mean monthly radiation to be drawn.

Other types of instruments sense only infrared radiation. One instrument, the *net radiometer*, can measure the difference between incoming radiation from above and outgoing radiation from below.

B. MEASUREMENT OF ATMOSPHERIC TEMPERATURE

Air temperature is a measure of sensible energy, a form of energy present in the air. This energy exists in the form of the high-speed motion of the gas molecules, which is greater with increased temperature. We cannot measure molecular activity directly, but only indirectly through its effect in changing the volume or electrical property of a sensing element exposed to the air.

The common *liquid-in-glass thermometer* serves well for most weather observations at stations near the ground and takes advantage of the principle that the expansion of fluid in the thermometer bulb is directly proportional to the temperature (Figure 4.2). By using a tube of extremely narrow but uniform diameter, small changes in temperature are detected by the relatively large changes in length of the liquid column. Mercury or alcohol is used in these thermometers.

A pair of specially constructed thermometers, one to record maximum temperature of a given period and the other to record minimum temperature of the same period, are standard equipment in the thermometer shelters at observing stations. The maximum-minimum thermometer pair is read daily and the two extreme values recorded.

Another principle is demonstrated by the *compound-metal (bimetallic) thermometer,* in

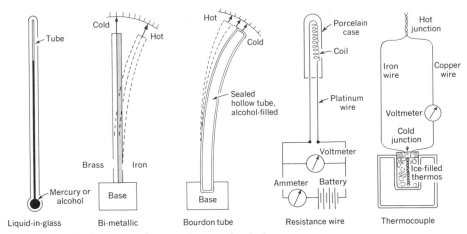

Figure 4.2. Principles used in five types of temperature-sensing devices.

which strips of two different metals (brass and iron) are bonded together into a single strip. Because one metal has a different coefficient of expansion than the other, the strip bends as the temperature rises and, in so doing, moves a pointer on a calibrated dial. A third type of thermometer uses the *Bourdon tube,* a hollow curved metal tube filled with liquid. When heated, the liquid expands, straightening the tube and thereby moving an indicator hand.

Still a fourth principle is used in the *electrical-resistance thermometer,* which consists of a thin platinum wire encased in a porcelain tube. The resistance of the wire to passage of an electric current increases with temperature, which can be measured with sensitive electrical meters. A fifth principle is utilized by the *thermocouple,* which uses two wires or strips of unlike metals joined together in a loop, or circuit, and connected to a sensitive voltmeter; difference in temperature between hot and cold junctions of the two metals sets up a weak electric current, whose strength varies with the temperature difference. The same principle is used in the pyrheliometer for the measurement of solar radiation.

Although the liquid-in-glass thermometer is the standard instrument for observing air temperature near the ground, it is fragile and cannot record temperatures automatically, but must be read by an observer. The metallic and electrical types not only are compact and sturdy, but will operate automatic recording devices as well. Therefore they are used in places where a continuous record is to be made and where the instruments are inaccessible or out of sight, as on sounding balloons sent up through the atmosphere, below ground for soil-temperature studies, or under water.

Temperature scales commonly used in weather science are the *Fahrenheit* and *Celsius* scales (Figure 4.3). On the Fahrenheit scale (designated as ° F), the freezing temperature of water is 32° F and the boiling point of water is 212° F. The Fahrenheit scale is not only in general use in the United States in everyday life, but also in the reports of surface weather conditions issued by the National Weather Service. The Celsius scale (designated ° C) takes 0° C for the freezing point and 100° C for the boiling point of water. The Celsius scale is used for upper-air weather observations in the United States. It is also used in Great Britain, Europe, and in various branches of science. Fahrenheit temperatures may be converted to Celsius, and vice versa, by use of the graphic scale or formulas in Figure 4.3. (The use of F° or C° following a number indicates a temperature range rather than a specific temperature; i.e., 6 F° is read as "six Fahrenheit degrees," not as "six degrees Fahrenheit.")

In stating temperatures in the upper atmo-

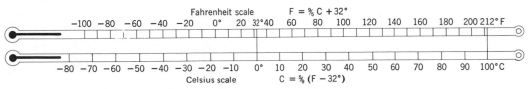

Figure 4.3. Comparison of Fahrenheit and Celsius scales. (© 1960, John Wiley & Sons, New York.)

sphere and for any mathematical scientific research, the *absolute Celsius scale* (or *Kelvin scale*) is used. This scale has the same degree units as the ordinary *Celsius* scale, but has the zero point at −273° C, a value known as *absolute zero*, or 0° K.

C. MEASUREMENT OF BAROMETRIC PRESSURE

Atmospheric pressure, or *barometric pressure,* one of the physical properties of weather measured routinely at all observing stations, is an essential part of all weather description and forecasts. Atmospheric pressure has an average value at sea level of 14.7 lb/in.² (about 1 kg/cm²) (Figure 4.4*A*).

Air pressure can be demonstrated and measured by a very simple device, the *mercurial barometer* (Figure 4.4*B*). The demonstration is often called Torricelli's experiment, after the man who first performed it in 1643. A glass tube of very narrow bore and about 36 in. (90 cm) in length is sealed at one end, filled with mercury, and inserted open end down into a dish of mer-

cury. Instead of pouring out of the tube, the mercury column stands at rest with a height of about 30 in. (76 cm), a vacuum occupying the section of empty tube above it. We may imagine that the mercury column in the tube represents the balancing weight on the scales in Figure 4.4*A*. In other words, a square column of mercury 1 in. thick and 30 in. high actually weighs as much as the entire column of atmosphere 1 in. square in cross section extending from the solid earth to interplanetary space. The exact average height of the mercury column at sea level is 29.92 in., which is taken as the standard sea-level pressure of the atmosphere. In metric units the established value is 76 cm, or 760 mm.

The mercurial barometer, although serving as the standard instrument for measurement of barometric pressure, is replaced by the *aneroid barometer*, where portability and resistance to rough handling are essential requirements. The principle of the aneroid instrument is illustrated in Figure 4.5; the instrument itself is shown in Figure 4.6. A flexible metal diaphragm, covering a sealed and partly evacuated metal chamber, moves in response to pressure changes. The movement of the diaphragm is greatly magnified by a mechanical system, and the pressure is read directly from the position of a pointer on a calibrated dial.

In modern weather science, air pressure is stated in somewhat different units, those of force per unit area; this system has the advantage of being independent of the density of any fluid. The unit is the *millibar*, 1013.2 millibars being equal to 29.92 in. (76 cm) of mercury. The millibar is one-thousandth of a *bar*, which is defined by physicists as a force of one million dynes per square centimeter of surface. The dyne in turn is defined as the force necessary to give a

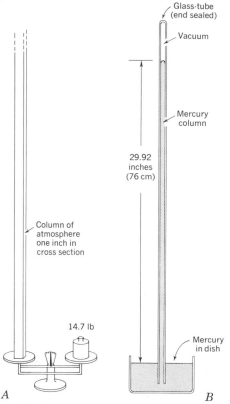

Figure 4.4. (*A*) Atmospheric pressure as the weight of a unit column of air, (*B*) Principle of the mercurial barometer.

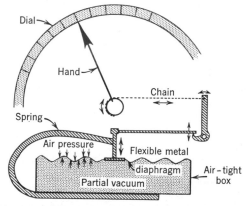

Figure 4.5. Mechanism of the aneroid barometer. (© 1960, John Wiley & Sons, New York.)

Figure 4.6. An aneroid barometer. (Taylor Instrument Company, Rochester, New York, Manufacturer. Photograph by courtesy of Science Associates, Inc.)

mass of 1 gm an acceleration of 1 cm per second per second. Because all three systems of stating pressure—inches, millimeters, and millibars—are used today in weather reports and maps, it is useful to know all three.

A continuous record of barometric pressure is obtained with the *barograph,* an instrument consisting of a pen-arm attached to an aneroid barometer mechanism (Figure 4.7). The pen

Figure 4.7. A continuous graph of barometric pressure change is made by this automatic recording barograph. (Photograph by NOAA National Weather Service.)

point makes a trace upon a sheet of graph paper wrapped around a drum turning slowly by a

clockwork mechanism. The barograph trace in Figure 4.8 shows the pressure drop and rise during passage of a hurricane.

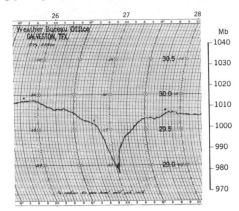

Figure 4.8. During the hurricane of July 27, 1943, a barograph in Galveston, Texas, recorded this trace of the fall and rise of pressure. (NOAA National Weather Service.)

D. MEASUREMENT OF WINDS

Wind velocity is a vector quantity, requiring statement of both direction and speed. Wind direction is stated as the direction from which the wind is blowing and may be indicated either by 8 or 16 compass points or by azimuth in degrees (see Figure 4.12). Thus a north wind comes from the north point of the compass—the air is traveling southward. Of all weather-observing instruments, perhaps the oldest and simplest is the familiar wind vane, from which the direction of surface winds is determined. Most wind vanes have a point, or arrowhead, which faces into the wind. Therefore one may simply read the compass direction toward which the arrow is pointing.

The instrument which measures wind speed is the *anemometer.* Several types are in use. The cup anemometer consists of three or four cups mounted at the tips of wheellike spokes turning horizontally on a delicate bearing (Figure 4.9). The cups travel at a speed approximately equal to the wind speed. The instrument can be so calibrated that the number of turns per minute is exactly equal to the wind speed in miles per hour. In other cup anemometers the turning shaft drives a small dynamo whose varying current is read on a sensitive ammeter calibrated in units of wind speed. Other types of anemometers measure the wind force on an exposed surface or against the air column in a tube whose open end is pointed into the wind.

To determine wind direction and speed in the air layer from near the ground surface up to

Figure 4.9. A three-cup anemometer. Dial below gives count of revolution. (NOAA National Weather Service.)

about 15,000 ft (5 km), pilot balloons filled with hydrogen or helium are released at the weather-observing station and tracked, as they ascend, by use of a telescopic instrument known as a *theodolite*. The rate of rise of the balloon is known and is constant. Consequently, if the vertical angle of sight is read at intervals of, say, 1 min, the horizontal distance of travel and wind speed can be calculated (Figure 4.10). The azimuth will indi-

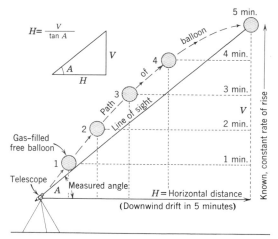

Figure 4.10. Downwind speed of a rising balloon can be calculated from the angle of a sight line upon it. (© 1960, John Wiley & Sons, New York.)

cate wind direction. Larger balloons carrying a reflective target are also tracked by radar, making possible observations above overcast layers or during precipitation.

Modern weather science requires accurate knowledge of wind direction and speed to the top of the troposphere and higher. To obtain this information—along with information on air temperature, air pressure, and water vapor content—the upper atmosphere must be sounded by sending up balloons carrying compact sensing instruments and a radio transmitter, which sends the information by code to a ground receiving station. This apparatus is named the *radiosonde*. An extension of this system, *rawinsonde*, uses a ground radio station to track the position of a radiosonde and thus to determine the direction and speed of winds at various levels up to great heights.

Wind speed is stated in statute miles per hour, in meters per second, or in knots (nautical miles per hour), knots being the preferred units for stating wind speeds in the troposphere. On weather maps wind direction and speed are indicated by a symbol resembling an arrow shaft with feathers, or barbs (Figure 4.11). On upper-air

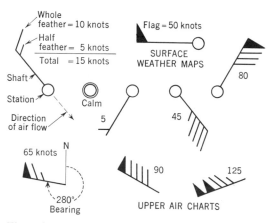

Figure 4.11. Direction and speed of winds is given by means of standard map symbols. (© 1960, John Wiley & Sons, New York.)

charts the direction is measured clockwise from geographic north, using the azimuth (full-circle bearing) system used in navigation (Figure 4.12).

E. WORLD MAPS OF SEA-SURFACE TEMPERATURES

Global distribution of sea-surface temperatures is shown by means of isothermal maps (Figure 4.13). These maps are drawn for the months of February and August, which are the months of extreme temperatures over the oceans as a whole. In general, isotherms of sea-surface temperatures run east-west. At about the 60th parallel of latitude, sea-surface temperatures are 0° C (32° F)

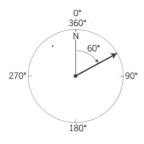

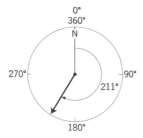

Figure 4.12. Azimuths are used to designate direction of upper-air winds. (© 1960, John Wiley & Sons, New York.)

or a little colder. The freezing point of sea water ranges from 28° to 31° F (−2.2° to −0.6° C), which means that sea water will remain liquid at temperatures somewhat lower than the freezing point of fresh water. Southward temperatures increase generally to reach a maximum of 28° to 29° C (83° to 84° F) over a broad belt of ocean in the equatorial latitudes.

Upsetting the east-west pattern of isotherms are marked equatorward bends in isotherms close to the west coasts of Africa, North America, and South America. This deflection results from cool equatorward currents and the upwelling of cold subsurface water. Similar but opposite bends in isotherms off the eastern coasts of Asia and North America reflect north-moving warm currents without upwelling.

Annual range in sea-surface temperatures is shown by meridional profiles—one representing the Atlantic Ocean, the other representing the Pacific Ocean (Figure 4.14). Annual range is greatest between 35° and 50° N, where it is on the order of 8 to 10 C° (14 to 18 F°). In the Southern Hemisphere, maximum range occurs in a lower latitude belt (30° to 40° S) and amounts to only 5 to 6 C° (11 to 13 F°).

Greater range over the Northern Hemisphere oceans is attributed to the influence of very cold air generated over the adjacent continents in winter. This cold air moving over the sea surfaces withdraws heat from the water by evaporation and convection. No comparable effect is found

in the Southern Hemisphere, where the ocean surface forms a single circumglobal belt in middle latitudes.

Annual range is very small in the equatorial belt, falling to less than 1 C° (1.8 F°) at about 5° N latitude in the Atlantic Ocean. The uniformly high incoming solar radiation in this belt explains the small temperature range.

F. WORLD MAPS OF AIR TEMPERATURES

The principles of air temperature control by land and water bodies, by latitude, and by altitude enable us to understand the general global air temperature pattern and its yearly changes. Distribution of temperatures over a large area is best studied by means of *isothermal maps,* on which lines are drawn to connect all places having the same temperature. Isothermal maps can be prepared not only for the temperatures observed at a given time, but also for the average monthly temperatures. Figures 4.15 and 4.16 show average monthly isotherms for the entire earth for the two months generally having the maximum and minimum temperatures over the continental areas: January and July. Isotherms have been generalized over the major mountain belts and high plateaus.

Notice first on these world air temperature maps that the isotherms trend generally east-west, following the trend of the parallels of latitude, as we should expect because of the diminishing solar radiation from equator to poles. The east-west trend is most clearly seen in the Southern Hemisphere, where a great expanse of ocean gives a single uniform type of surface around the entire globe in the middle latitudes. In the Northern Hemisphere, however, the two great land masses of Eurasia and North America disrupt the east-west pattern and cause centers of higher or lower temperature to develop seasonally.

In January a *cold pole,* averaging below −50° F (−46° C) forms over northern Siberia with somewhat less severely cold centers over the Greenland icecap and the Alaska-Yukon region. In contrast, in July the land areas heat intensely to produce high-temperature centers over North Africa, southern Asia, and the Sonoran Desert region of Mexico and the southwestern United States. A monthly mean exceeding 100° F (38° C) is found in a small part of the western Sahara. These hot centers are also very dry and constitute the great tropical deserts. T' ir Southern Hemisphere counterparts are seen on the January map in the high-temperature zones over southwest Africa and central Australia, but mean val-

AUGUST

FEBRUARY

Figure 4.13. Sea-surface temperatures (°C) for the months of August and February. (Fahrenheit equivalents are given in parentheses.) [Simplified from H. U. Sverdrup (1942), *Oceanography for Meteorologists*, Englewood Cliffs, N.J., Prentice-Hall. Map based on Goode Base Map. Copyright by Univ. of Chicago; used by permission of Univ. of Chi-

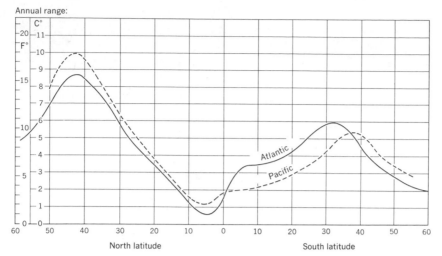

Figure 4.14. Meridional profiles of the mean annual range of surface-water temperatures in the Atlantic and Pacific Oceans. [After H. U. Sverdrup, M. W. Johnson, and R. H. Fleming (© 1942, renewed 1970), *The Oceans,* Englewood Cliffs, N.J., Prentice-Hall, p. 130, Figure 31.]

ues are not as high as in the Northern Hemisphere deserts.

Antarctica shows very well the effect of a continent centered on a pole and covered by a vast icecap. The isotherms run in roughly concentric circles around the south pole and indicate bitterly cold winter averages. In summer (January) the snow-covered surfaces reflect so much radiation that temperatures average below $-20°F$ ($-30°C$), even though the south pole receives more radiation in a 24-hr day in January than the equator does in a day at equinox. The extreme cold is in an air layer close to the ground, for a few hundred feet above the surface the air may be as much as 50 F° (28 C°) warmer. Their high altitude is a major contributing factor to extreme cold of both Antarctica and Greenland.

Over the Arctic Ocean winter temperatures do not drop to the extreme low levels found in Siberia, Antarctica, or the Greenland icecap, because some heat is conducted to the air from the water, through the floating layer of sea ice. Thus the ocean shows its moderating influence, even at the north pole.

A comparison of January and July temperatures at various points in the middle latitudes confirms the principle of land and water contrasts. Isotherms are deflected poleward over the continents in summer and equatorward over the continents in winter. Over the oceans a given isotherm shifts north and south through only about 5° of latitude, whereas on land it migrates through 15-30° of latitude.

G. WORLD MAPS OF BAROMETRIC PRESSURES AND WINDS

(Figures 4.17 and 4.18)

H. WORLD OCEAN CURRENTS

Figure 4.19 shows world patterns of ocean currents and drifts. The westward drifts of water in equatorial latitudes are referred to as the *North Equatorial Current* and *South Equatorial Current.* These are separated by the *Equatorial Countercurrent* that moves eastward and is caused by the return of lighter surface water which has been piled up on the western side of the ocean basin by the equatorial currents. The Equatorial Countercurrent is best developed in the Pacific Ocean, but is also found in the Atlantic and Indian Oceans.

The intensification of poleward currents on the western sides of the North Atlantic and North Pacific Oceans results in two powerful warm currents, the *Gulf Stream* in the Atlantic and *Kuroshio Current* in the Pacific. Speeds up to 5 knots (2.6 m/sec) are developed in these narrow streams. Perhaps most familiar of all currents to Americans is the Gulf Stream, which flows northward from the Caribbean, passing close to Florida and the southeast Atlantic coast, then curving northeast to spread over the North Atlantic. The Kuroshio Current is a similar warm current of the western Pacific. It sets in close to the Philippines, running northeastward past Formosa and the southern islands of Japan. In the Southern Hemi-

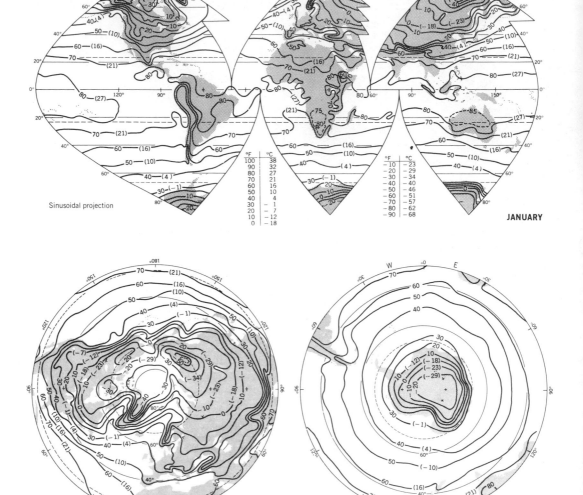

Figure 4.15. Mean January surface-air temperatures, °F. (Equivalent centigrade temperatures in parentheses.) [Isotherms compiled by John E. Oliver from data by World Climatology Branch, Meteorological Office, *Tables of Temperature, 1958,* Her Majesty's Stationery Office, London; U.S. Navy (1955), *Marine Climatic Atlas,* Washington, D.C.; and P. C. Dalrymple (1966), Amer. Geophys. Union. Isotherms reproduced by permission of John Wiley & Sons, New York.]

sphere similar but less intensively developed currents flow southward off the coasts of Australia *(East Australia Current)* and South America *(Brazil Current).*

Upon turning eastward, each warm poleward current becomes part of the *west-wind drift,* produced by the highly variable prevailing westerly winds in latitude 40° to 65°. The gyre is then completed by a cold coastal current moving equatorward close to the western coast of the bordering continent. The four most important examples

are the *California Current, Canary Current, Peru* or *Humboldt Current,* and *Benguela Current.* Upwelling, explained by the drift of water away from the coast as well as the importation of cold water from the high latitudes, makes these coastal currents unusually cold, considering their low-latitude locations. Fog produced by condensation of water vapor in air cooled close to the sea surface hangs over these currents for long periods of time. Air temperatures are surprisingly cool throughout the year for latitudes at which we

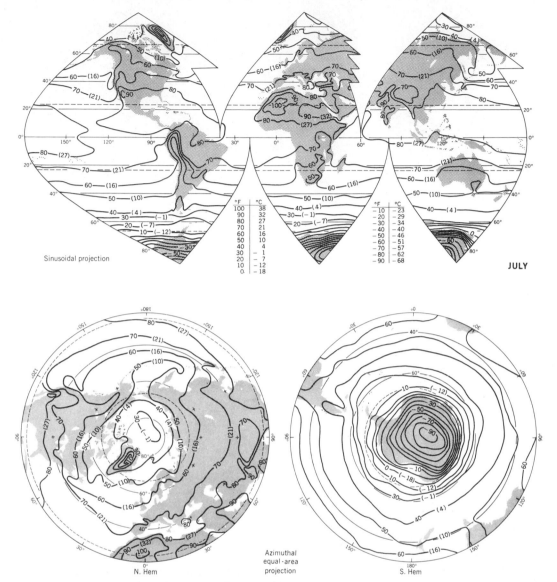

Figure 4.16. Mean July surface-air temperatures, °F. (Equivalent centigrade temperatures in parentheses.) (Same data sources as Figure 4.15. Isotherms reproduced by permission of John Wiley & Sons, New York.)

find the world's hottest deserts not far inland. The 70° F isotherm for January and July (Figures 4.15 and 4.16) shows a strong equatorward bend in crossing the cool current, but a poleward bend in crossing the warm current on the western side of the ocean.

The *North Atlantic drift,* an eastward movement of warm water, divides upon approaching western Europe. While part turns southward to form the Canary Current, most continues northeast to the British Isles, where a strong current passes just north of Scotland and thence northeast along the Norwegian coast, as the *Norway*

Current, to the Arctic Ocean well above the Arctic Circle. Murmansk, an ice-free port on the Arctic Circle, owes its year-round navigability to the Norway Current, for the polar sea would otherwise freeze over solidly in winter at this high latitude.

Surface-water movements in the arctic and antarctic regions must be considered separately from one another because of the exactly opposite relationship between land and water. The Arctic Ocean is an open ocean centered approximately on the north pole and fringed by lands between which straits provide a connection with

Figure 4.17. Average January surface barometric pressures in millibars, reduced to sea level. Only the last two digits are shown. Arrows showing prevailing winds are drawn to agree with isobars. (Map compiled by John E. Oliver from data by Y. Mintz, G. Dean, R. Geiger, and J. Blüthagen. Isobars reproduced by permission of John Wiley & Sons, New York.)

the Pacific and Atlantic basins. On the other hand, the Southern Hemisphere extremity consists of a pole-centered landmass, Antarctica, about the same size as the Arctic Ocean but completely surrounded by an open ocean, the Southern Ocean.

Currents in the Arctic Ocean take the form of a single large gyre of clockwise motion centered at about 80° N latitude in the Beaufort Sea directly north of Alaska. Arctic water flows south in vigorous cold currents entering the North Atlantic. One of these is the *Labrador Current,* which flows south through Baffin Bay

and Davis Strait to reach the Labrador coast and Newfoundland. It is this cold water, meeting the warm water of the Gulf Stream in the vicinity of the Grand Banks of Newfoundland, that gives rise to great advection fogs. Along the east side of Greenland is another stream of cold arctic water flowing south. This is the *East Greenland Current,* a rapid stream which passes between Greenland and Iceland to mix with the North Atlantic drift. Outflow of cold water is largely equaled by inflow of warmer water by the Norwegian Current.

The Southern (Antarctic) Ocean, which is sim-

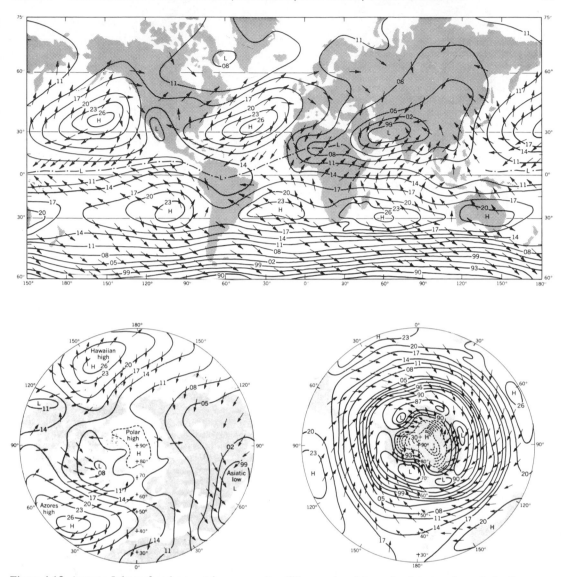

Figure 4.18. Average July surface barometric pressure in millibars, reduced to sea level, and surface winds. (Same data sources as Figure 4.17. Isobars reproduced by permission of John Wiley & Sons, New York.)

ply the southern part of the Pacific, Atlantic, and Indian Oceans in the region of the 50th and 60th parallels, forms a continuous circular ribbon of ocean, scarcely interrupted by land (Figure 4.20). Here the *Antarctic Circumpolar Current* flows eastward in an uninterrupted path following the parallels of latitude. This current represents the joining of west-wind drifts of the individual ocean basins under the prevailing westerly winds.

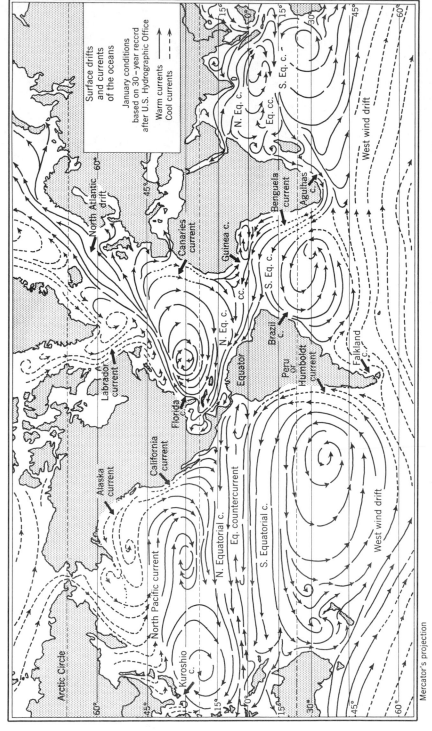

Figure 4.19. World map of average surface drifts and currents of the oceans for the month of January. (Based upon data of the U.S. Navy Oceanographic Office. ©1960, John Wiley & Sons, New York.)

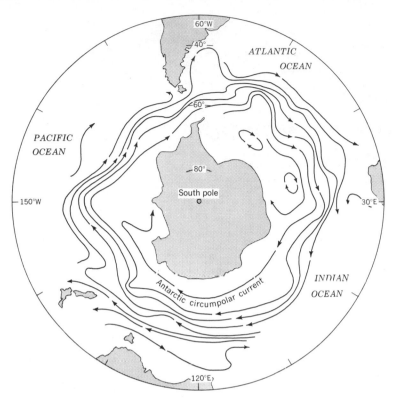

Figure 4.20. Streamlines of water flow about the Antarctic continent. Where lines are most closely spaced, rate of flow is most rapid. [After H. U. Sverdrup (1942), *Oceanography for Meteorologists,* Englewood Cliffs, N.J., Prentice-Hall, p. 206, Figure 57.]

BANK 5
ATMOSPHERIC MOISTURE
AND CYCLONIC STORMS

A. MEASUREMENT OF RELATIVE HUMIDITY

Instruments for the measurement of the water-vapor content of air may use one of two principles. The *hygrometer,* on whose scale relative humidity is read directly, makes use of a human hair, or other suitable fiber, which lengthens as humidity increases and shortens as it decreases. Change in length of the hair can be made to activate an arm to which a pen is attached, thus drawing a continuous line on a slowly turning drum. Such an apparatus is known as a *recording hygrograph.*

The principle of varying rates of evaporation is made use of in the *sling psychrometer,* an instrument consisting of two liquid-in-glass thermometers mounted side by side (Figure 5.1).

Figure 5.1. A sling psychrometer. (Photograph by NOAA National Weather Service.)

One thermometer has its bulb exposed to the air, as usual, whereas the other has a piece of water-saturated cloth wrapped around its bulb. The thermometer pair is swung through the air by means of a handle and swivel joint, so that evaporation cools the wet bulb, depressing its temperature somewhat below that of the dry bulb. The degree of cooling of the wet bulb depends upon the dryness of the air. For fully saturated air no evaporation will occur and both thermometers will read the same. In dry air the wet-bulb thermometer will register a temperature several degrees below that of the dry bulb. By means of a standard table (Table 5.1) or by using a specially calibrated slide rule, it is possible to estimate relative humidity from the temperature difference of the two bulbs.

B. CLOUD FAMILIES AND TYPES

Clouds are grouped into classes and named according to height and general form, whether stratiform or cumuliform. An international system of classification recognizes four families of clouds: *high clouds, middle clouds, low clouds,* and *clouds of vertical development* (Figure 5.2).

The high-cloud family above 23,000 ft (7 km) includes individual types named *cirrus, cirrocumulus,* and *cirrostratus.* All are composed of ice crystals. Cirrus is a wispy, featherlike cloud, commonly forming streaks or plumes named *mares' tails* (Figure 5.3A). Cirrus clouds are so thin as to make no barrier to sunlight. Cirrocumulus is a layer composed of small cumulus masses looking like tiny bits of cotton (Figure 5.3B). The regular geometric pattern formed by these cloud masses is sometimes described as a *mackerel sky.* Cirrostratus is a thin veillike cloud, commonly causing a halo around the sun or moon but too thin to dim sunlight appreciably. The halo is evidence that the cloud particles consist of ice rather than of liquid water. Cirrus clouds, particularly the streaked cirrus bands, on occasion indicate the presence of a high-altitude jet stream, with the wind direction paralleling the long lines of the cloud.

The middle-cloud family, extending from 6,500 to 23,000 ft (2 to 7 km) in height, includes two cloud types—*altocumulus* and *altostratus.* Altocumulus consists of grayish cumuliform cloud masses lying in a distinct layer, with blue sky visible in breaks between masses (Figure

Table 5.1. RELATIVE HUMIDITY TABLE

°F	Difference Between Dry and Wet Bulbs																																							
	½°	1°	1½°	2°	2½°	3°	3½°	4°	4½°	5°	6°	7°	8°	9°	10°	11°	12°	13°	14°	15°	16°	17°	18°	19°	20°
30°	94	89	83	78	73	67	62	56	51	46	36	26	16	6											
35°	95	91	86	81	77	72	67	63	58	54	45	36	27	19	10	2									
40°	96	92	87	83	79	75	71	68	64	60	52	45	37	29	22	15	7								
45°	96	93	89	86	82	78	74	71	67	64	57	51	44	38	31	25	18	12	6						
50°	96	93	90	87	83	80	77	74	71	67	61	55	49	43	38	32	27	21	16	10	5				
55°	97	94	91	88	85	82	79	76	73	70	65	59	54	49	43	38	33	28	23	19	14	9	5		
60°	97	94	91	89	86	83	81	78	75	73	68	63	58	53	48	43	39	34	30	26	21	17	13	9	5
65°	97	95	92	90	87	85	82	80	77	75	70	66	61	56	52	48	44	39	35	31	27	24	20	16	12
70°	98	95	93	90	88	86	83	81	79	77	72	68	64	59	55	51	48	44	40	36	33	29	25	22	19
75°	98	96	93	91	89	86	84	82	80	78	74	70	66	62	58	54	51	47	44	40	37	34	30	27	24
80°	98	96	94	91	89	87	85	83	81	79	75	72	68	64	61	57	54	50	47	44	41	38	35	30	27
85°		96		92		88		84		81	77	73	70	66	63	60	57	53	50	47	41	38	35	32	29
90°		96		92		89		85		81	78	74	71	68	65	61	58	55	52	49	47	44	41	39	36
95°		96		93		89		86		82	79	76	73	69	66	63	61	58	55	52	50	47	44	42	39
100°		96		93		89		86		83	80	77	73	70	68	65	62	59	56	54	51	49	46	44	41

Dry-Bulb Temperature (row labels at left)

Note: Take dry-bulb temperature (left) closest to observed dry-bulb thermometer reading. Follow this row to the right to the column containing the observed difference between dry- and wet-bulb thermometer readings. The number in the body of the table is the *relative humidity* (percentage).

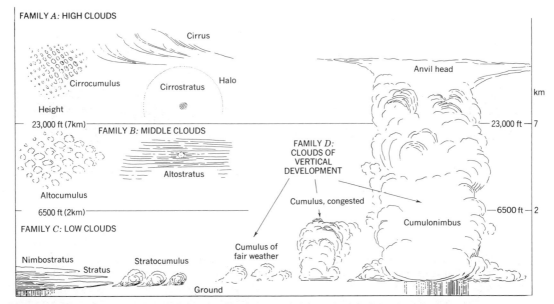

Figure 5.2. Cloud forms are classified into families based on height and vertical development.

5.3C). Altocumulus is usually associated with fair weather. Altostratus is a rather uniform thick grayish blanket, usually with a smooth underside, and is a frequent precipitation pro-ducer. It will shut out sunlight, but the sun can be seen as a bright spot through the cloud (Figure 5.3D).

The low-cloud family, found from ground

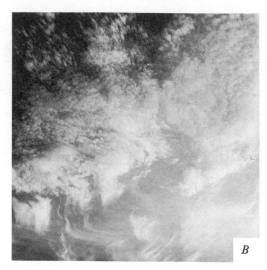

Figure 5.3. High-cloud forms. (*A*) Fibrous form of cirrus clouds. (*B*) Cirrocumulus (above) and tufted cirrus (below). (Photographs by F. Ellerman; NOAA National Weather Service.)

Middle and low clouds. (*C*) Active form of altocumulus. (Photograph by C. F. Brooks; NOAA National Weather Service.) (*D*) Thin altostratus with fractostratus patches below. The sun shows as a bright spot of light. (Photograph by G. A. Clarke; NOAA National Weather Service.)

level to a height of 6500 ft (2 km) above the earth's surface (not necessarily measured from sea level), includes three types: *stratus, nimbostratus,* and *stratocumulus.* Stratus is a low, uniform cloud sheet at low height and usually completely covers the sky. The gray undersurface is foglike in appearance. Where stratus thickens to the point that rain or snow begins to fall from it, the cloud becomes designated nimbostratus, the prefix "nimbo" meaning rain. Normally, nimbostratus will be dense and dark gray, shutting out much daylight. The cloud may extend upward

many thousands of feet into the middle-cloud height range (altostratus can also be nimbostratus). Ragged cloud patches beneath the nimbostratus are named *fractostratus* or *scud.*

Stratocumulus consists of low individual masses of dense cloud, the masses forming a distinct layer with an approximately uniform base. The masses are dark gray on the shaded sides, but white on the illuminated sides often with narrow breaks between them through which blue sky is visible. Stratocumulus is produced by rather intense turbulent motions of the air rising

Cumuliform clouds. (*E*) Cumulus of fair weather. (Photograph by H. T. Floreen, NOAA National Weather Service.) (*F*) Cumulonimbus. This isolated thunderstorm has heavy rain falling from the central region. (Photograph by Air Service, U.S. Navy. NOAA National Weather Service.)

and sinking within the cloud layer. Stratocumulus is best developed in the clearing period following a cyclonic storm, when gusty cold winds are blowing. Brief rain or snow squalls may develop from the cloud masses. Viewed from above, in sunlight, stratocumulus is like a vast white quilt.

Clouds of the fourth family, those of vertical or upright development, are all the cumuliform type. The smallest and most pleasant are the simple *cumulus of fair weather*. These are snow-white cottonlike clouds, generally with rounded tops and rather flattened bases (Figure 5.3*E*); their shaded undersides are gray. On the whole the accompanying weather is fair with much sunshine. Small cumulus may grow larger and denser to form *congested cumulus* with rounded tops resembling heads of cauliflower and flat dark-gray bases. These larger cumulus in turn may grow into gigantic *cumulonimbus* clouds, or thunderheads, from which come violent rain, hail, wind gusts, and thunder and lightning (Figure 5.3*F*). Cumulonimbus clouds on occasion extend upward to heights of 60,000 ft (18 km) in the tropics and thus occupy low-, middle-, and high-cloud zones simultaneously.

A class of cloud quite different in origin and significance from those described above is the *wave cloud*, distinguished by the fact that the cloud itself remains stationary with respect to some topographic feature on the ground, while at the same time air moves rapidly through the cloud form. Air motion is in the form of a *stationary wave*.

Figure 5.4 illustrates two occurrences of wave clouds. With strong winds present, air is forced to ascend while passing over a topographic obstacle such as a hilltop or ridge (Figure 5.4*A*). Under favorable combinations of temperature and humidity, moisture in the rising air condenses to produce a lenticular cloud (Figure 5.5). As the air descends to the lee of the obstacle, adiabatic warming causes the cloud to evaporate. The cloud is thus constantly in a state of both condensation on its windward side and evaporation on its leeward side while remaining in a fixed position.

Where strong winds blow over a high mountain crest, the air flow is thrown into a succession of stationary waves to the lee of the crest (Figure 5.4*B*). Here, again, conditions may be favorable for the development of the lenticular cloud, one at each wave crest. *Mountain waves,* as this form of air disturbance is often termed, constitute a severe hazard to aircraft, both because of the extreme turbulence that may be present and because of a strong downdraft immediately in the lee of the range.

C. MEASUREMENT OF PRECIPITATION

Precipitation is stated in terms of depth in inches or millimeters and represents the depth of water that would be caught in a straight-sided flat-bottomed pan from which there is no loss by

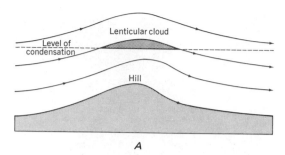

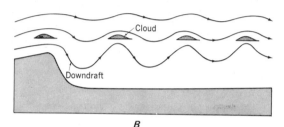

Figure 5.4. (A) Lenticular cloud over a hilltop.
(B) Wave clouds in lee of a mountain crest.

Figure 5.5. A lenticular cloud, holding a stationary position over a hill summit. (NOAA National Weather Service.)

Figure 5.6. A tipping-bucket rain gauge of standard design used in a weather-observing station. (NOAA National Weather Service.)

evaporation. The *rain gauge,* one of the simplest of weather instruments, consists of a cylinder 4 or 8 in. (10 or 20 cm) in diameter leading into a funnel which collects the water in a long narrow tube in which small amounts can be measured easily by inserting a calibrated stick (Figure 5.6). Some types are able to weight the water and record the amounts automatically.

Snow may be measured by sampling the snow depth and converting the average figure into the equivalent of water, which is commonly one-tenth the depth of the snow. Very loose freshly fallen snow may, however, reduce to as little as one-thirtieth of its depth as water. If the funnel of the rain gauge is taken out, the cylinder can be used to catch a snowfall, which is then melted to determine its water equivalent. For estimates of snow equivalents on mountain slopes where snow has accumulated over long periods and has layers varying in degree of density, a thin-walled cylinder is forced into the snow to obtain a sample, which is then weighed.

In describing precipitation amount, not only must the depth be given, but the period of time must be given as well. Thus the cumulative total depths to fall in a month or year constitute the *monthly* or *yearly (annual) precipitation,* respectively. Total depth for single storms is also commonly given. The *intensity* of precipitation is determined by the amount falling in very short periods of time, as in 1 hr, or in one 10-min period. Intensity of 0.1 in. (2.5 mm) per hour would be considered a moderate rain, whereas 1 in. (25 mm) per hour would constitute a real cloudburst, causing storm drains to back up and flood city streets.

D. WORLD PRECIPITATION TYPES

The areal extent of precipitation can be shown on a map by means of lines of equal amounts of

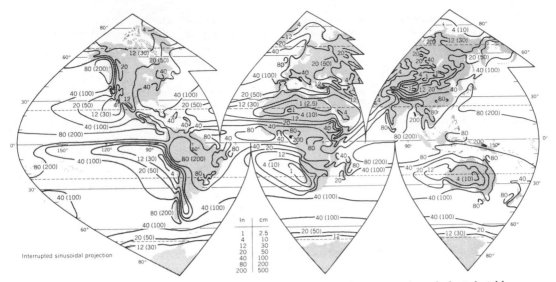

Figure 5.7. World map of mean annual precipitation. Isohyets in inches of water; metric equivalents in table. (Isohyets modified and simplified from *The Times Atlas*, 1958, *World Climatology*, Volume 1, Plate 3, London, The Times Publ. Co.)

precipitation, or *isohyets*. A given isohyet connects all points on the map having a specified quantity of rainfall in a given period of time. Figure 5.7 shows average annual precipitation for the entire world, exclusive of the polar regions. The map is generalized and does not show details of precipitation differences, but it reveals a global pattern of seven types:

(1) The *wet equatorial belt* of heavy rainfall, over 80 in. (2030 mm) annually, straddles the equator and includes the Amazon River basin in South America, the Congo River basin of equatorial Africa, much of the African coast from Nigeria west to Guinea, and the East Indies. Here the prevailingly warm temperatures and high moisture content of the air favor abundant convective rainfall. Thunderstorms are frequent and their great cumulonimbus clouds extend upward to heights as great as 50,000-60,000 ft (15-18 km).

(2) Narrow coastal belts of high rainfall, 60-80+ in. (1520-2030+ mm) per year, extend from near the equator to latitudes of about 25° to 30° N and S on the eastern sides of every continent or large island. For examples, see the eastern coasts of Brazil, Central America, Madagascar, and northeastern Australia. These are the *trade-wind coasts,* or *windward tropical coasts,* where moist air from warm oceans is brought over the land by the trades. Encountering coastal hills, escarpments, or mountains, these winds produce heavy orographic rainfall.

(3) In striking contrast to the wet equatorial

belt astride the equator are the two zones of huge *tropical deserts* lying approximately upon the Tropics of Cancer and Capicorn. These hot, barren deserts, with less than 10 in. (254 mm) of rainfall annually and in many places with less than 2 in. (50 mm), are located under and caused by the subtropical cells of high pressure where the subsiding air is adiabatically warmed and dried. Note that these deserts extend off the west coasts of the lands and out over the oceans. Such rain as these areas experience is largely convectional and extremely unreliable.

(4) Farther northward, in the interiors of Asia and North America between latitude 30° and latitude 50°, are great continental *middle-latitude deserts* and expanses of semiarid grasslands known as *steppes.* Dryness here results from remoteness from ocean sources of moisture. Located in a region of prevailing westerly winds, these arid lands occupy the position of rain shadows in the lee of coastal mountains and highlands. Thus the Cordilleran Ranges of Oregon, Washington, British Columbia, and Alaska shield the interior of North America from moist air originating in the Pacific. Upon descending into the intermontane basins and interior plains, this air is warmed and dried.

Similarly, mountains of Europe and the Scandinavian peninsula serve to obstruct the flow of moist air from the North Atlantic into western Asia. The great southern Asiatic ranges likewise prevent the entry of moist tropical air from the Indian Ocean and the western Pacific.

The Southern Hemisphere has too little land in the middle latitudes to produce a true continental desert, but the dry steppes of Patagonia lying on the lee side of the Andean chain are roughly the counterpart of the North American deserts and steppes of Oregon and northern Nevada, which lie in the rain shadow of the Sierra Nevada and the Cascade Range.

(5) On the southeastern sides of the continents of North America and Asia, in latitude 25° to 45°, and to a less marked degree in these same latitudes in the Southern Hemisphere in Uruguay, Argentina, and southeastern Australia, are the *humid subtropical* regions with 40-60 in. (1020-1520 mm) of rainfall annually. These regions lie on the moist western sides of the subtropical high-pressure centers in such a position that humid air from the tropical ocean is carried poleward over the adjoining land. Commonly, too, these areas receive heavy rains from tropical storms.

(6) Still another distinctive wet location is on *middle-latitude west coasts* of all continents and large islands lying between about 35° and 65° in the region of prevailing westerly winds. These zones have already been explained as good examples of coasts on which abundant orographic precipitation falls. Where the coasts are mountainous, as in Alaska and British Columbia, Patagonia, Scotland, Norway, and South Island of New Zealand, the annual precipitation is over 80 in. (2030 mm). Small wonder that these coasts formerly supported great valley glaciers which carved the deep bays known as fiords, so typically a part of their scenery.

(7) The seventh precipitation region is formed by the *arctic* and *polar deserts*. Northward of the 60th parallel, annual precipitation is largely under 10 in. (254 mm), except for the west-coast belts. Cold air cannot hold much moisture; consequently it does not yield large amounts of precipitation. At the same time, however, the relative humidity is high and evaporation is low. Consequently these arctic and polar regions have abundant moisture in the air and soil and are not to be considered as dry in the same sense as the tropical deserts.

E. CYCLONIC STORM ON THE SURFACE MAP*

Further details and characteristics of a wave cyclone are illustrated in Figure 5.8, in which two

*Text and two weather maps in this section are from A. N. Strahler, *Introduction to Physical Geography.* Copyright © 1965 by John Wiley & Sons, Inc., New York. Reproduced by permission of the publisher.

weather maps are shown. These have been redrawn with only slight changes from the National Weather Service daily maps for April 3 and 4, 1963. Map *A* shows a cyclone in a stage approximately equivalent to block *B* of Figure 5.15 in *Planet Earth.* The storm is centered over western Minnesota and is moving northeastward. Notice the following points: (a) Isobars of the low are closed to form an oval-shaped pattern. (b) Isobars make a sharp V where crossing the cold front. (c) Wind directions, indicated by arrows, are at an angle to the trend of the isobars and form a pattern of counterclockwise in spiraling. (d) In the warm-air sector, there is northward flow of tropical air toward the direction of the warm front. (e) There is a sudden shift of wind direction accompanying the passage of the cold front, as indicated by the widely different wind directions at stations close to the cold front, but on opposite sides. (f) There is a severe drop in temperature accompanying the passage of the cold front, as shown by differences in temperature readings at stations on either side of the cold front. (g) Precipitation, shown by shading, is over a broad zone near the warm front and in the central area of the cyclone, but extends as a thin band down the length of the cold front. (h) Cloudiness, shown by degree of blackness of station circles, is greatest in the warm sector and northeastern part of the cyclone, but the western part is virtually clear. (i) The low is followed on the west by a high (anticyclone) in which low temperatures and clear skies prevail. (j) The 32° F (0°C) isotherm crosses the cyclone diagonally from northeast to southwest, showing that the southeastern part is warmer than the northwestern part.

A cross section through map *A* along the line *AA'* shows how the fronts and clouds are related. Along the warm front is a broad area of stratiform clouds. These take the form of a wedge with a thin leading edge of cirrus. Westward this thickens to altostratus, then to stratus, and finally to nimbostratus with steady rain. Within the warm air mass sector, the sky may partially clear with scattered cumulus. Along the cold front are violent thunderstorms with heavy rains, but this is along a narrow belt that passes quickly.

The second weather map, map *B,* shows conditions 24 hr later. The cyclone has moved rapidly northeastward into Canada, its path shown by the line labeled *storm track.* The center has moved about 800 mi (1300 km) in 24 hr, a speed of just over 40 mi (65 km) per hour. The cyclone has occluded. An occluded front replaces the separate warm and cold fronts in the central part of the disturbance. The high-pressure area, or tongue of cold polar air, has moved in to the west and south of the cyclone, and the cold front is passing over the eastern and Gulf Coast states. Within closed isobars around the anticyclone, the skies are clear and winds are weak. In another day the entire storm will have passed out to sea, leaving the eastern United States in the grip of cold but clear weather. A cross section below the map shows conditions along the line BB', cutting through the occluded part of the storm. Observe that the warm air mass is being lifted higher off the ground and is giving heavy precipitation.

F. CYCLONE DEVELOPMENT UNDER AN UPPER-AIR WAVE

Figure 5.9 is a series of weather maps of North America illustrating the relation between wave cyclones and the larger upper-air waves. The lower line of charts shows conditions at about 18,000-19,000 ft (5.5-5.8 km). The continuous lines on the map are not actually isobars, but may be considered equivalent to isobars for purposes of comparing the two maps. Actually, the pressure lines on the upper-air map are contours representing the elevation of the 500-mb pressure surface. In a way this is a map of the topography of an imaginary surface at which the pressure is everywhere the same. Thus high altitude corresponds to high pressure. The upper-air charts show conditions several hours later than the surface charts, but this does not greatly alter the general points of comparison.

On November 17 an upper-air wave trough lies over the western United States. The air in this trough is very cold, $-30°$ F ($-34°$ C) over Wyoming at 18,000 ft (5.5 km). At the ground

surface there is an east-west stationary front oriented from Texas to North Carolina. This is the line between cold (*cP*) air on the north and warm (*mT*) air on the south and represents conditions at the outset of the life cycle of the wave cyclone. A wave is already beginning to form over the Rio Grande Valley, as shown by a weak low-pressure center with cold and warm fronts. This low lies on the southeast margin of the upper-air wave.

On November 18 the upper-air wave has deepened and has shifted eastward. Note that the air flow at high levels parallels the isobars and that there is very little suggestion of the well-developed wave cyclone that is now in the open stage of development and is centered over the Ohio Valley. The cyclone at low levels is located on the eastern side of the upper-air wave but is traveling rapidly northeast, as if dragged along and steered by the strong northeastward air flow at high levels. Note the divergence shown above the center of the low.

On November 19 the cyclone is in the occluded stage, centered over Lake Superior. Over this same position on the upper-air map is a nearly circular low with counterclockwise air flow. This represents the cutting off of the upper-air wave to form an isolated pocket of cold air. Meantime the tongue of the cold *cP* air mass which invaded the Central States behind the surface cold front of the wave cyclone has now spread far over the Gulf of Mexico, but nevertheless the upper-air winds are westerly in this same area. On the final map, November 20, the wave cyclone has moved over Labrador, heading for the North Atlantic, while the upper-air wave has also moved farther east.

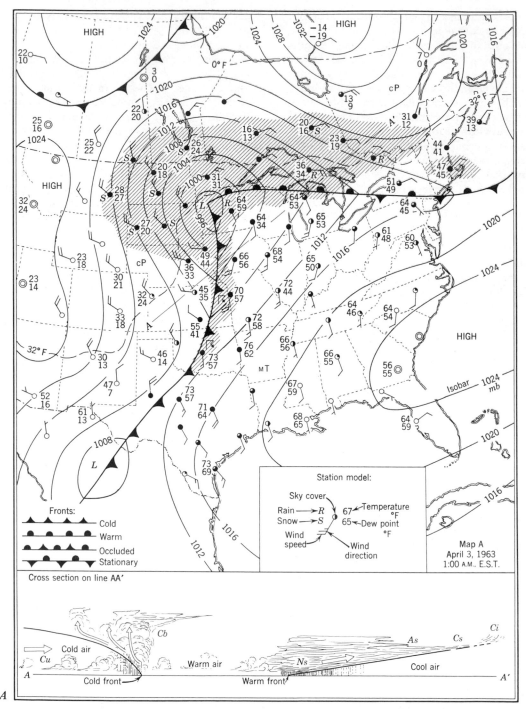

Figure 5.8. Surface weather maps from two successive days show the development and movement of a middle-latitude cyclone. Temperature and dew point are in °F. Areas having precipitation are shaded. (Modified and simplified from maps of NOAA National Weather Service. Copyright ©1965, John Wiley & Sons, New York.)

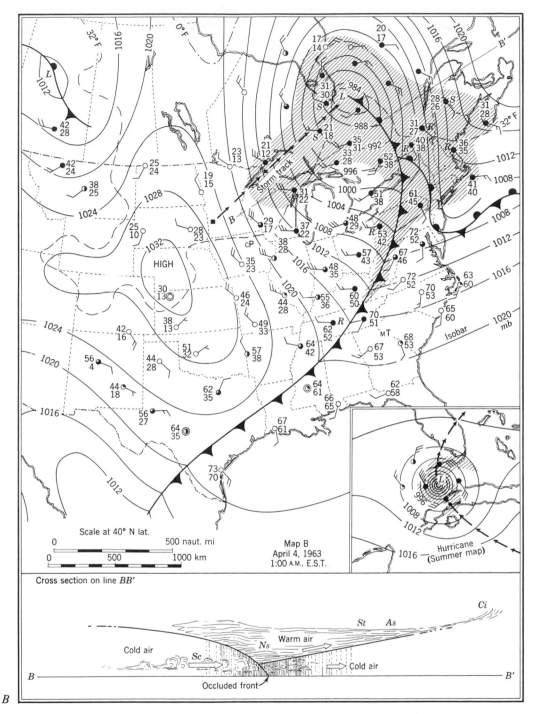

Figure 5.8. (*Continued*)

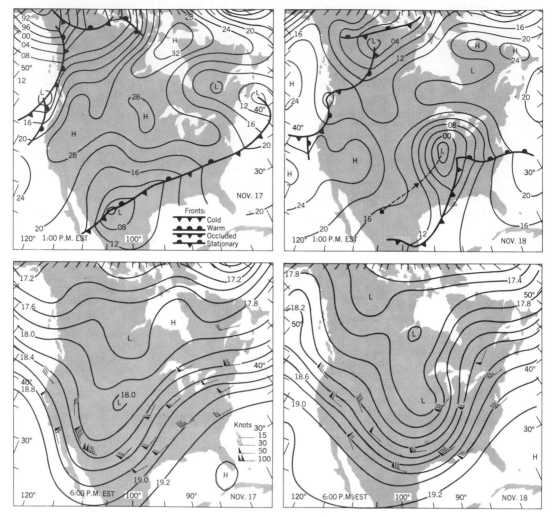

Figure 5.9. Weather maps for four consecutive days showing evolution and movement of an intense cyclonic storm and its relation to upper-air pressure and winds. *Upper row*: Surface maps for 1:00 PM EST. Isobars in millibars, labeled with last two digits. *Lower row*: Pressure and winds in the altitude range 17,000 to 19,000 ft. Contours drawn on the 500-mb surface, labeled in thousands of feet. Note that data for upper-air maps are gathered 6 to 10 hr later than that for surface maps. (Redrawn and simplified from NOAA National Weather Service daily weather maps.)

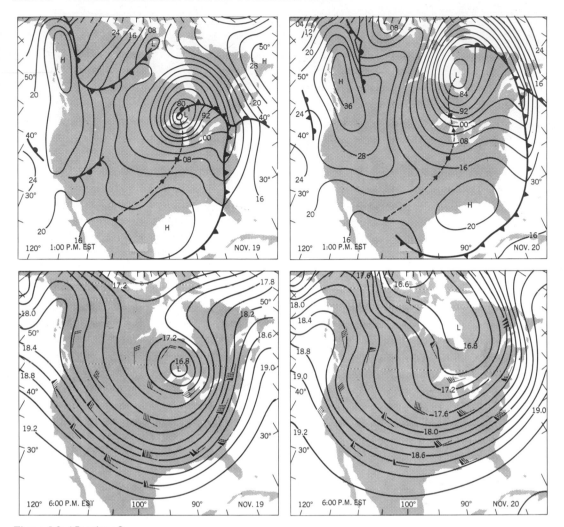

Figure 5.9. (*Continued*)

BANK 6
STREAM SYSTEMS

A. STREAM GAUGING

The responsibility of measuring, or *gauging,* the principal streams of the United States is in the hands of the U.S. Geological Survey, through its Water Resources Division. Cooperating with state and municipal agencies, the Geological Survey maintains over 6000 gauging stations on the nation's principal streams and their tributaries.

meter is lowered into the water at regular intervals of horizontal distance and depth so as to give the average velocity at each of many points, forming a regular grid pattern over the entire cross section (Figure 6.1). The current meter consists of a set of revolving cups whose rate of turning is proportional to the stream velocity (Figure 6.2). The turning of the cups causes an electric circuit to be broken repeatedly, sending

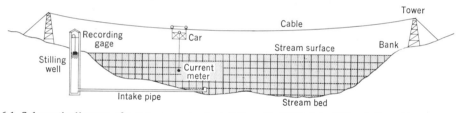

Figure 6.1. Schematic diagram of a stream-gauging installation. (© 1960, John Wiley & Sons, New York.)

Discharge figures, published in a series of water-supply papers, provide essential information for the planning of flood-control devices and the construction of dams for water power and irrigation.

The simplest measurement to be taken is that of the height of stream surface, termed the *stage.* This may be done by attaching a scaled rod, or *staff gauge,* to a bridge pier or abutment, where it can be read directly as required. When a continuous record of stage is needed, a *stilling tower* is constructed beside the stream (Figure 6.1). This structure is merely a masonry or concrete *stilling well* connected by a pipe to the stream channel so that the water level in the well matches that of the stream surface. A float, connected by a wire to a recording mechanism, rises and falls with the water level and produces a continuous record of stage.

Determination of stream discharge requires that the cross-sectional area and mean velocity be measured directly. For this purpose a *current*

Figure 6.2. Stream-gauging apparatus for use on a large river. A convenient bridge permits the current meter (*right*) to be lowered by a power winch at any desired point. (Photograph by U.S. Geological Survey.)

a series of clicks to headphones worn by the observer. A count of the clicks in a given span of time will establish the velocity.

The Price current meter, shown in Figure 6.2, is capable of measuring velocities in the range from 0.2 to 20 ft (0.06 to 6 m) per second. Measurements can be made from a bridge or, where no bridge is available, from a cable car running on a cable suspended across the river (Figure 6.1). Depth measurements are made along with the current measurement, making it possible to determine a profile of the stream bed and the stream's cross-sectional area. Mean velocity can be computed by averaging the individual readings of the entire cross section. Discharge then follows from the formula $Q = AV$.

Obviously stream gauging requires considerable time and effort, and it would not be practical to carry on a continuous series of current-meter readings. Fortunately, a simple method of estimating discharge by means of stage reading alone is available in the *rating curve,* or *stage-discharge curve* (Figure 6.3). To prepare such a

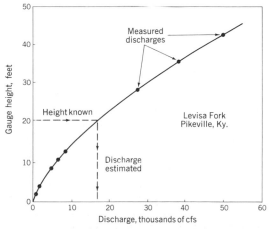

Figure 6.3. By means of this rating curve the discharge of Levisa Fork, Kentucky, could be estimated from stream stage. The curve shown here was used in the period October, 1945, to January, 1946. [© 1960, John Wiley & Sons, New York. Data from W. G. Hoyt and W. B. Langbein (1955), *Floods,* Princeton, N.J., Princeton Univ. Press, p. 69, Figure 23.]

curve, discharge is measured by current meter for several discharges covering a wide range of values. These data are plotted on a graph of stage (gauge height) versus discharge, and a smooth curve is drawn to connect and extend the points. Once drawn, the curve serves to give a quick estimate of discharge for any measured stage. For example, in Figure 6.3 a stage height of 20 ft gives an estimated discharge of about

16,500 cfs. Rating curves must be recomputed and corrected at intervals of time because the channel form may change somewhat through flood erosion. The curves are most effective when used in a highly stable reach of a river, as where bridges and other engineering works give the channel a fixed form.

B. RELATION OF STREAM VELOCITY TO DEPTH AND SLOPE

Hydraulic engineers have tried for almost two centuries to establish a useful mathematical relationship among observed values of stream velocity and both depth and gradient (slope). First to make this attempt was a French engineer, whose formula of 1775 is known as the *Chezy equation*:

$$V = C\sqrt{R \cdot S}$$

where V is mean stream velocity, R is hydraulic radius, and S is slope, as percent grade. The term C is a numerical constant. Hydraulic radius is defined as the area of cross section divided by the wetted perimeter. We can rewrite the Chezy equation as follows:

$$V = C \cdot \sqrt{R} \cdot \sqrt{S}$$
or
$$V = C \cdot R^{1/2} \cdot S^{1/2}$$

In words, this equation states that the mean velocity varies as the square root of hydraulic radius and as the square root of slope.

Hydraulic radius is essentially equivalent to the average stream depth. An increase of velocity with increase in depth is to be expected (when slope is held constant) because the frictional resistance with the bed has less influence for deeper water than for shallower. The increase of velocity with steeper slope (holding depth constant) is intuitively obvious, since the component of gravitational force acting parallel with the stream bed is greater when slope is steeper.

That velocity increases about as square root of slope can be easily demonstrated with a small laboratory flume of rectangular cross section. By means of blocks the flume can be raised successively through slopes of 1, 2, 3, and 4 percent. By controlling the flow of water, depth can be kept constant at all values of slope, although the discharge must also be increased to maintain constant depth. Surface velocity is measured by timing the travel of floating particles, and this is converted to mean velocity by multiplying by 0.7. Mean velocity can also be derived by measuring the discharge of the flume and dividing by cross-sectional area. Table 6.1 summarizes the

Table 6.1. EXPERIMENTAL FLUME DATA ON RELATION OF VELOCITY TO SLOPE

Slope	Square Root of Slope	Observed Mean Velocity, cm/sec	Calculated Mean Velocity ($V = Q/A$), cm/sec
0.01	0.100	23.2	21.7
0.02	0.141	33.8	32.2
0.03	0.173	40.5	39.6
0.04	0.200	48.0	48.0

Source: Data obtained by A. N. Strahler.

data of a typical experiment. The plotted points in Figure 6.4 show reasonably close approximation to a straight line, as required by the Chezy equation.

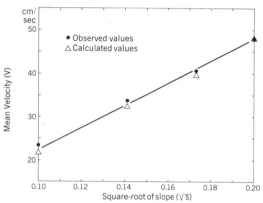

Figure 6.4. Plot of mean velocity against square root of slope. (Data from Table 6.1.)

The Chezy equation has been revised a number of times on the basis of additional measurements. In wide use today is the *Manning equation:*

$$V = \frac{1}{n} R^{2/3} \cdot S^{1/2}$$

While the square root relationship remains unchanged for slope, the exponent for hydraulic radius has been raised to the two-thirds power. The constant, n, is a numerical estimate of the roughness of the stream bed, and measures the total effect of various forms of irregularities in the configuration of the bed and alignment of the channel. When cgs units are used, the value of n runs from 0.015 to 0.060 in natural streams.

C. GEOMETRICAL LAWS OF STREAM NETWORKS AND DRAINAGE BASINS

If we are given a map of a complete stream-channel network of a drainage basin, as shown in Figure 6.5, it is possible to subdivide the net in-

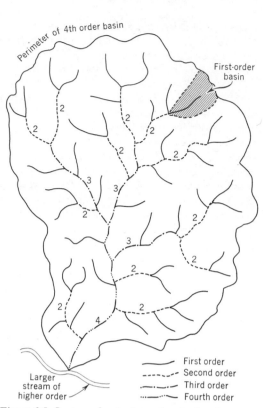

Figure 6.5. System of assigning orders to the stream segments within a drainage basin. (© 1960, John Wiley & Sons, New York.)

to individual *channel segments,* defined by stream junctions, and to designate by integer numbers the segments in terms of orders of magnitude within a hierarchy. Every fingertip channel, from its point of origin to its first point of junction, is designated as a channel segment of the *first order*. The junction of any two first-order channels produces a segment of the *second order*, the junction of any two second-order segments produces a segment of the *third order,* and so forth. The junction of a single first-order segment with a second-order or higher-order channel does not, however, produce any change in the order of the segment it joins.

When this ordering system is applied throughout the entire drainage network, it will be found that a single trunk-stream segment bears the highest-order designation. Where a large stream network is taken into consideration, the order of any segment will, on the average, reflect the magnitude of the channel in terms of its channel dimensions, discharge, and contributing watershed area. A relatively large sample must be taken to reveal consistent relations, because individual segments may be much longer or shorter than the average and there will be many chance

Table 6.2. STREAM ORDERS AND NUMBERS, BIG BADLANDS, SOUTH DAKOTA

Stream Order	Number of Stream Segments	Bifurcation Ratio
1	139	
		3.02
2	46	
		4.18
3	11	
		3.66
4	3	
		3.00
5	1	

Source: Data from K. G. Smith (1958), *Bull. Geol. Soc. Amer.*, vol. 69, pp. 975-1008 (see Figure 14).

distortions in the pattern of the network.

The first step in stream-network analysis is to count the numbers of stream segments of each order. The example in Table 6.2 is taken from a carefully surveyed detailed map of a small drainage network typical of the Big Badlands of South Dakota.

The ratio of the number of stream segments of a given order to the number of segments of the next higher order is termed the *bifurcation ratio*. In the example cited above, this ratio ranges from as low as 3 to over 4 between the various orders. These observed differences can be attributed to chance variations that may affect any stream network.

The accumulated data of many stream networks involving thousands of stream segments have revealed the principle that in an area of uniform climate, uniform rock type, and uniform history of geologic development the bifurcation ratio tends to be constant from one order to the next, hence that a single ratio characterizes the entire network. Commonly the bifurcation ratio falls between 3 and 5. Rarely is the theoretical minimum possible value of 2 approached.

There follows from observation a *law of stream numbers:* The numbers of stream segments of successively lower orders in a given basin tend to form a geometric progression, commencing with a single trunk segment of the highest order and increasing according to a constant bifurcation ratio. For example, given a bifurcation ratio of exactly 3 and a trunk-stream segment of the sixth order, the numbers of segments within the system will be 1, 3, 9, 27, 81, and 243.

Any geometric progression, such as the number series 1, 3, 9, 27, 81, 243, represents a constant ratio of increase. Therefore, if we should plot the numbers of stream segments on a constant-ratio (logarithmic) scale against stream

orders on a uniform (arithmetic) scale, the points should fall close to a straight line. Figure 6.6 shows the data of Table 6.2 plotted on such a

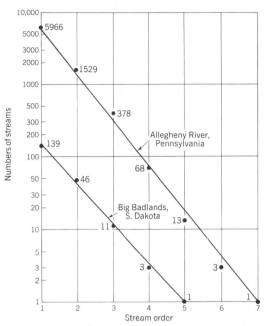

Figure 6.6. Plot of numbers of stream segments against stream order for two stream systems of vastly different size. The plotted information is also given in Tables 6.2 and 6.3. [Data of Marie E. Morisawa (1962) and Kenneth G. Smith (1958).]

graph, known as a *semilogarithmic plot.* The five points do not conform exactly with the fitted straight line, but departures from this line are small.

Table 6.3 gives network data for a large portion of a drainage basin, that of the Allegheny River in the Appalachian Plateau region of Pennsylvania. Numbers of stream segments for this basin are also plotted against order in Figure 6.6.

Inspection of the segments of various orders in Figure 6.5 shows that on the average the second-order segments are longer than those of first order, that third-order segments are longer than second-order segments, etc. To study this matter further, examine the data of Table 6.3 for the Allegheny River drainage basin.

Although the master stream of this basin is given as of the seventh order, its length and area are stated with reference to a stream gauge and do not reveal the full segment dimensions. Therefore only the first six orders should be considered in analyzing the data.

The mean length of segments of each order is converted into *cumulative mean length,* by

Table 6.3. ALLEGHENY RIVER DRAINAGE BASIN CHARACTERISTICS

Stream Order	Number of Segments	Bifurcation Ratio	Mean Length of Segments, miles	Cumulative Mean Length, miles	Length Ratio	Average Watershed Area, square miles
1	5966		0.09	0.09		0.05
		3.9			3.3	
2	1529		0.3	0.4		0.15
		4.0			2.7	
3	378		0.8	1.2		0.86
		5.7			3.1	
4	68		2.5	3.9		6.1
		5.3			2.8	
5	13		7	11		34
		4.3			2.9	
6	3		20	31		242
		3.0				
7	1		8 + (not complete)			550 (not complete)

Source: Data from Marie E. Morisawa (1962), *Bull. Geol. Soc. Amer.*, vol. 73, see p. 1037.

adding the mean length of each order to the sum of those of lower orders. When this is done, the cumulative mean length of segments of any order is approximately three times the average cumulative length of segments of the next lower order, this relation being expressed by the *length ratio*.

Extensive observations of drainage networks show that the cumulative length ratio tends to remain constant within a given drainage system. It is therefore possible to state a *law of stream lengths*: The cumulative mean lengths of stream segments of successively higher orders tend to form a geometric progression beginning with the cumulative mean length of the first-order segments and increasing according to the length ratio.

Figure 6.7 shows the cumulative length data of Table 6.3 in a semilogarithmic plot against stream order. Except for the first-order segments, all points lie very close to the fitted straight line. Also shown on this same graph is a plot of cumulative length data for Fern Canyon, a small watershed in the San Gabriel Mountains of California.

Each first-order stream segment of a drainage network receives runoff as overland flow from contributing slopes of a *first-order basin*, examples of which are shown in Figure 6.8. A second-order basin includes two or more first-order basins, in addition to which there are *interbasin areas* from which overland flow passes directly into the second-order channel segment. Thus the basin area of a segment of any higher order includes all areas of basins of lower orders in the system, plus all interbasin areas. Studies of many drainage basins have shown

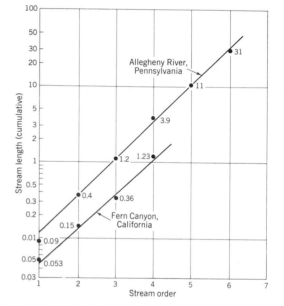

Figure 6.7. Plot of cumulative mean stream length against stream order. [Data of Marie E. Morisawa (1962) and James C. Maxwell (1960).]

that basin area tends to increase with order in a manner similar to that shown by increase of cumulative stream length with order. This relationship is stated in a third law of drainage basin geometry: The mean basin areas of successive stream orders tend to form a geometric series beginning with mean area of the first-order basins and increasing according to a constant area ratio. Figure 6.9 is a semilogarithmic plot of basin area against order for the Allegheny River data of Table 6.3 and for Fern Canyon, California.

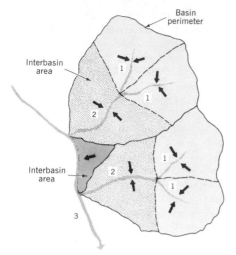

Figure 6.8. Nested arrangement of basins of first and second orders with interbasin areas.

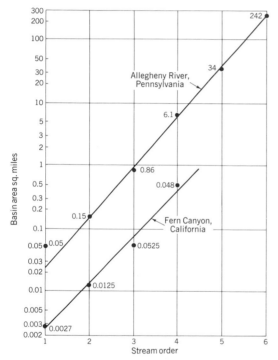

Figure 6.9. Plot of mean basin area against stream order. [Data of Marie E. Morisawa (1962) and James C. Maxwell (1960).]

An almost universal characteristic of drainage basins that have had ample time to adjust their geometry to prevailing conditions of hydrology and geology is that the slope, or gradient, of the first-order streams is, on the average, steeper than the average slope of the second-order streams, and that the average gradient diminishes with each integer increase in order. (Reasons for

Table 6.4. CHANNEL SLOPES OF THE HOME CREEK, OHIO, DRAINAGE BASIN

Order	Mean Channel Slope	Slope Ratio
1	0.181	
		0.48
2	0.087	
		0.32
3	0.028	
		0.32
4	0.009	
		0.56
5	0.005	

Source: Data from Marie E. Morisawa, 1959.

this downstream decrease in channel slope are explained in *Planet Earth.*)

The nature of downstream decrease in channel slopes can be seen in an example for which data are given in Table 6.4. For each stream order in the drainage basin of Home Creek, Ohio, the mean channel slope is given as a ratio of vertical drop to horizontal distance. The *slope ratio,* or ratio of mean slope of one order to that of the next higher order, is given in a third column. In this example the ratios range from about one-half to one-third, with an average of about 0.4.

On the basis of extensive data on channel slopes, a law of stream slopes has been formulated: The mean slopes of stream segments of successively higher orders in a given basin tend to form an inverse geometric series, decreasing according to a constant slope ratio.

Figure 6.10 is a semilogarithmic plot of mean channel slope against stream order for the data of Home Creek. The data conform rather well to the requirements of the law of stream slopes, but with deviations that are to be expected in a natural system.

The laws of stream numbers, lengths, basin areas, and channel slopes were derived by a distinguished hydrologist, Robert E. Horton, on the basis of actual stream network data and are empirical in nature. Each law can be given formal statement as a mathematical equation. Together these laws can be regarded as a modern quantitative expression of Playfair's law of 1802 to the effect that streams run in valleys proportioned to their sizes and that they have a good adjustment of their declivities (slopes).

Horton's laws can be expressed as equations, using the following terms:

u designation of order, an integer number, 1, 2, 3, etc.

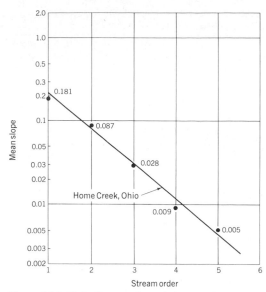

Figure 6.10. Plot of mean channel slope against stream order. [Data of Marie E. Morisawa (1959).]

N_u Number of streams of order u
R_b bifurcation ratio, defined as $N_u/N_u + 1$
k order of the main trunk segment
$\overline{L}_u$ mean length of stream segments of order u
R_L length ratio, defines as $\overline{L}_u \overline{L}_{u-1}$
$\overline{A}_u$ mean area of basins of order u
R_a area ratio, defined as $\overline{A}_u/\overline{A}_{u-1}$
$\overline{S}_u$ mean channel slope of segments of order u
R_s slope ratio, defined as $\overline{S}_u/\overline{S}_{u-1}$

Law of stream numbers

$$N_u = R_b{}^{(k-u)}$$

Law of stream lengths

$$\overline{L}_u = \overline{L}_1 R_L{}^{(u-1)}$$

where $\overline{L}_1$ is mean length of first-order segments.

Law of basin areas

$$\overline{A}_u = \overline{A}_1 R_a{}^{(u-1)}$$

where $\overline{A}_1$ is mean area of first-order segments.

Law of stream slopes

$$\overline{S}_u = \overline{S}_1 R_s{}^{(u-1)}$$

where $\overline{S}_1$ is mean slope of first-order segments.

D. STREAM DISCHARGE AND BASIN AREA

It is to be expected that the stream discharge will tend to increase with increasing basin area, since the discharge is derived from overland flow and ground-water seepage from precipitation falling upon that watershed. When the mean annual discharge, as calculated from stream gauge records, is plotted against the total area of watershed lying above that gauge, a simple relationship of discharge to basin area is revealed (Figure 6.11). Although the data are plotted on

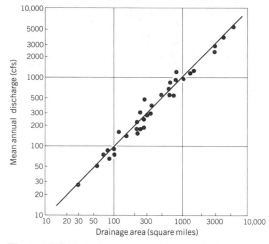

Figure 6.11. Plot of mean annual stream discharge against drainage basin area. [Data of John T. Hack (1957), *U.S. Geol. Surv. Professional Paper 294-B*, p. 54, Figure 15.]

a double-logarithmic graph, the straight line of best fit is so inclined that the discharge increases in direct proportion to the increase in drainage area. Once the existing relationship has been established for a given watershed, it is possible to make good estimates of the mean annual discharge at any given point on a trunk stream by merely measuring the watershed area lying above that point.

The observed relationship between discharge and area is expressed in the equation:

$$\overline{Q} = aA^b$$

where $\overline{Q}$ is mean annual discharge, A is basin area, and a and b are numerical constants. The value of b is close to 1.0.

E. DRAINAGE DENSITY

Drainage networks show a wide range in fineness or coarseness of pattern, just as a woven fabric can range from an extremely fine silk cloth to coarse burlap. In drainage systems the scale of fineness or coarseness of the pattern is described by a measure termed the *drainage density*, computed by measuring the total length of all channels in the basin and dividing by the area of the basin:

Drainage density $=\dfrac{\text{total length of stream channels, miles}}{\text{basin area, square miles}}$

If, for example, a drainage density of 15 is obtained, we can say that there are 15 mi of channel length for every square mile of surface. Metric units may also be used. To convert to kilometers per square kilometers, multiply drainage density values by 0.62.

Examples of various drainage densities are shown in Figure 6.12. Each map covers 1 mi² (2.6 km²). Map *A* illustrates very low drainage density, averaging from 3 to 4 mi of channel per square mile. Note that a single first-order drainage basin is over one-third of a mile across. Low drainage density, which we may also describe as *coarse texture*, is typical of regions of extremely resistant rock, particularly basins eroded in

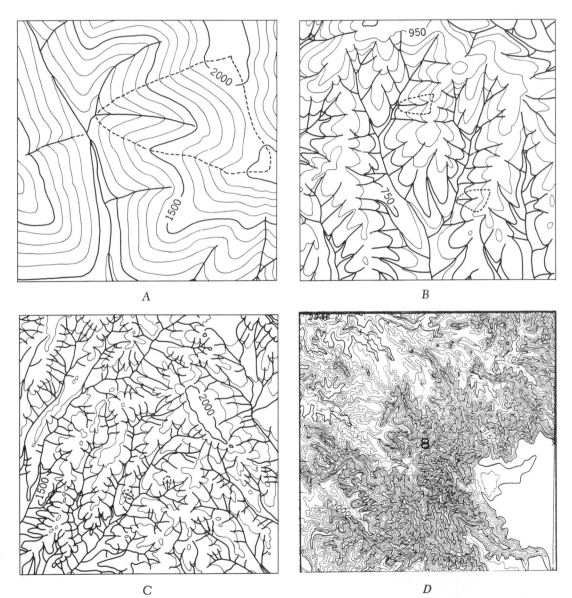

Figure 6.12. Each of the above maps covers 1 mi², but the total length of stream channels found in each area is greatly different from one map to the next. (© 1960, John Wiley & Sons, New York. Based on maps of the U.S. Geological Survey.) (*A*) Low drainage density (coarse texture) in Driftwood, Pennsylvania, quadrangle. (*B*) Medium drainage density (medium texture) in Nashville, Indiana, quadrangle. (*C*) High drainage density (fine texture) in Little Tujunga, California, quadrangle. (*D*) Badlands, where drainage density is extremely high (ultrafine texture) in Cuny Table West, South Dakota, quadrangle.

massive sandstone strata. Map *B* illustrates medium drainage density in the range 12 to 16. Such areas are widespread in humid climates of the central and eastern United States over a wide variety of rock types. Map *C* illustrates high drainage density, ranging from 30 to 40. Such *fine texture* is typical of regions of relatively weak rocks in a semiarid climate where vegetative cover is sparse. Map *D* illustrates *ultrafine texture* of drainage network with drainage density running from 200 to 400. This is an area of badlands.

Several factors control drainage density. Physical properties of the bedrock or overburden into which the valleys are carved is a primary control. If the region is one of very hard massive rock, such as granite or thick sandstone strata, drainage density tends to be low because a large surface area of runoff is required to produce the channel discharge needed to erode and maintain a channel in such rock. If the underlying ma-

terial is highly permeable, low drainage density will be favored because much of the precipitation is infiltrated and a large surface area is required to furnish the runoff needed for maintenance of a channel. If the underlying material is impermeable, as in a dense clay or shale, much of the precipitation runs off as overland flow and is therefore more effective in sustaining channels. Thus clay, which combines weakness with low permeability, yields the highest drainage densities. Still another factor is the presence of a vegetative cover. Where plant growth is dense, the surface is made more resistant to erosion, hence the drainage density tends to be lower than in a corresponding area barren of vegetation. We might also reason that in a region where rainfall is more intense, yielding more storm runoff, drainage density will tend to be higher than it would be in a region where rainfall intensity is lower.

BANK 7
SILICATE MINERALS
AND IGNEOUS ROCKS

A. CHEMICAL GROUPING OF MINERALS

Minerals can be classified according to chemical composition as well as by certain physical properties, such as crystal form and atomic structure. In terms of an understanding of the origin and distribution of rock varieties, the chemical grouping of common minerals will be the more meaningful approach. If, however, one's purpose is to be able to identify a given mineral or rock specimen by name, a knowledge of the mineral classifications based upon physical properties will be essential.

Minerals may be composed of single elements, or of compounds of those elements. Almost all common rock-forming minerals consist of compounds, the single-element minerals being comparative rarities. Table 7.1 lists several classes of inorganic compounds to which the most abundant minerals can be assigned. Representative examples of common minerals are given for each group. The groups as listed do not conform with a strictly formalized chemical classification, nor is the list of groups by any means complete. The information presented in Table 7.1 is intended only to give insight into the wide variety in chemical compositions and degrees of complexity to be expected among the common minerals.

B. PHYSICAL PROPERTIES OF MINERALS

An intensive laboratory course using mineral specimens and the equipment needed to perform various tests would be required to gain even a rudimentary understanding of the physical properties of the commonest minerals. In these paragraphs we can only suggest the types of physical properties that serve to differentiate minerals according to species.

Crystal form Most minerals occur in the crystalline solid state, in which the various component atoms, as ions, occupy regular positions in a characteristic geometrical arrangement known as a *crystal lattice*. The nature of crystalline structure is treated in later paragraphs. When a crystalline mineral grows without inhibition or interference from other minerals about it (for example, crystal growth in an aqueous solution or in soft mud), a distinctive geometric configuration of the mineral surfaces appears and is known as the *external crystal form*. Normally a crystal presents smooth planar surfaces, or *faces*, which together form a distinctive geometrical solid, such as the cube, prism, octahedron, or tetrahedron (Figure 7.1). Because the angles between various sets of crystal faces are constant for a given mineral species, measurements of the crystal configuration permit the mineral to be identified.

On the basis of symmetry, the crystal forms of minerals fall into *crystal systems*, of which there are six (Figure 7.1). For example, the mineral *diamond* falls into the *isometric system* and assumes the geometrical form of an octahedron. (The crystals of magnetite in Figure 8.15 in *Planet Earth* are octahedrons.) The mineral *quartz* falls into the *hexagonal system* and typically takes the form of a six-sided prism, terminating at each end in a hexagonal pyramid. These forms are seen in Figure 7.2.

Cleavage Many minerals show a pronounced tendency to split along smooth planar surfaces of weakness. These surfaces, known as *cleavage planes*, bear a close relationship to the external crystal form. One set of cleavage planes may be very strongly developed, as in the familiar case of mica, which can be split easily into thin sheets (see Figure 7.5). In other minerals there are three intersecting sets of parallel cleavage planes, enabling the mineral to be broken into similar prisms or rhombs of many sizes (see Figure 7.8

Table 7.1. SOME CHEMICAL CLASSES OF COMMON MINERALS

Chemical Group		Representative Mineral		Symbol
NATIVE ELEMENTS				
	Metals	Native copper		Cu
		Gold		Au
	Nonmetals	Native sulfur		S
		Diamond		C

	Description	Representative Mineral	Composition	Formula
COMPOUNDS				
Oxides	Elements in combination with oxygen	Quartz	Silicon dioxide	SiO_2
		Hematite	Sesquioxide of iron	Fe_2O_3
		Ice	Solid state of water	H_2O
Sulfides	Elements in combination with sulfur	Galena	Lead sulfide	PbS
		Sphalerite	Zinc sulfide	ZnS
Carbonates	Elements in combination with carbonate ion (CO_3)	Calcite	Calcium carbonate	$CaCO_3$
		Dolomite	Carbonate of calcium and magnesium	$CaMg(CO_3)_2$
Halides	Compounds of the halogen elements: chlorine, bromine, iodine, fluorine	Halite (rock salt)	Sodium chloride	NaCl
		Fluorite	Calcium fluoride	CaF_2
Sulfates	Elements in combination with sulfate ion (SO_4)	Anhydrite	Calcium sulfate	$CaSO_4$
		Gypsum	Hydrous calcium sulfate	$CaSO_4 \cdot 2H_2O$
Silicates	Elements in combination with silicate ion (SiO_4)	Orthoclase feldspar	Aluminosilicate of potassium and sodium	$(K,Na)AlSi_3O_8$
		Olivine	Silicate of magnesium and iron	$(Mg,Fe)_2SiO_4$
Hydrous silicates	(Clay minerals) Compounds derived by union of water with silicate minerals	Kaolinite	Hydrous aluminosilicate derived from feldspars	
		Illite	Complex hydrous aluminosilicate derived from micas	
Hydroxides	Compounds derived by union of water with oxides of the the metals iron, aluminum, manganese	Limonite	Hydrous sesquioxide of iron	$2Fe_2O_3 \cdot 3H_2O$
		Bauxite	Hydrous sesquioxide of aluminum	$Al_2O_3 \cdot 2H_2O$

and, in *Planet Earth,* Figure 8.19). The key to an understanding of mineral cleavage lies in the atomic structure of crystals.

Minerals lacking cleavage break along various characteristic forms of fracture surfaces. For example, the curved fracture surfaces of glass constitute *conchoidal fracture,* seen in quartz (Figure 7.2). Other fracture types are described as even, uneven, splintery, or hackly.

Specific gravity, or *relative density* For a given chemical composition, each mineral species has a fixed specific gravity, which is the ratio of its density to the density of water at 4° C (39.2° F). Most of the abundant minerals in igneous rocks have densities in the range of 2.7

(quartz) to 3.4 (olivine). Other minerals have much higher specific gravities—for example, hematite is about 5.0, galena 7.5, and native copper 8.8. Mineral specific gravity is a property of great importance because it determines the specific gravity of a given rock, which is a mixture of minerals, and rock specific gravity determines the gross layered structure of the earth.

Hardness The degree to which a mineral surface resists being scratched is known as its hardness and is a geologically important property because it determines how easily a mineral is worn away by abrasive action of streams, waves, wind, and glaciers in the processes of erosion and transportation. Minerals themselves provide

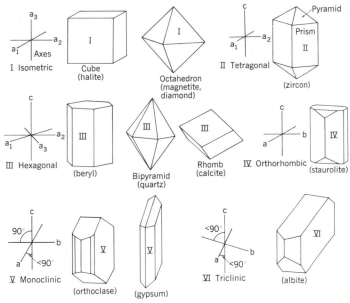

Figure 7.1. Axes and representative external crystal forms of the six crystal systems.

a set of tools of differing hardness by means of which other minerals can be tested. Ten standard minerals constitute the *Mohs scale* of hardness, ranging from the softest, talc (No. 1), to the hardest, diamond (No. 10). The complete scale is as follows:

1. talc (softest)
2. gypsum (2½, fingernail)
3. calcite (3, copper coin)
4. fluorite
5. apatite (5½ to 6, knife blade, plate glass)
6. orthoclase (6½ to 7, steel file)
7. quartz
8. topaz
9. corundum
10. diamond (hardest)

Each mineral on the scale will scratch all those of lower number, but will be scratched by those of higher number.

Luster The appearance of a mineral surface under reflected light is referred to as its luster, described by several descriptive adjectives, such as metallic, adamantine (diamondlike), vitreous, resinous, pearly, or silky.

Color Certain minerals possess a distinctive color that facilitates recognition, but many minerals have varieties that differ conspicuously in color. Among the rock-forming minerals the range is from colorless (quartz, calcite, gypsum) and white (orthoclase feldspar), through olive green (olivine) to black (biotite, hornblende). Reddish-brown and yellow-brown colors are typical of iron oxides such as hematite and limonite. These minerals lend earth-red coloration to many sedimentary rocks (red sandstones, red shales).

Streak When a mineral specimen is rubbed across the unglazed surface of a white porcelain plate, it may leave a streak of powdered mineral of distinctive color. This "streak" is consistently useful in identifying the mineral. An example is hematite, with a red-brown streak. Most common rock-forming minerals give a white streak of no particular help in identification.

Optical properties A completely different group of mineral properties relate to the effect of a transparent mineral upon light rays which pass through it. These optical properties are of great value in mineral identification and are evaluated by means of a polarizing microscope. A particularly important diagnostic property is the degree to which the mineral bends (refracts) light rays passing through it.

C. SILICATE MINERALS

Table 7.2 gives properties of the principal silicate minerals of the most common igneous rocks.

Quartz consists of silica, an oxide of silicon (SiO_2). It is one of the commonest of minerals among rocks of all three major groups. A hard mineral (hardness 7) lacking in cleavage, quartz when clear has an outward resemblance to broken glass, as seen in the massive state (Figure 7.2*B*). The characteristic pyramid-topped hex-

Table 7.2. SILICATE MINERALS ABUNDANT IN IGNEOUS ROCKS

Mineral or Group	Composition, Formula	Specific Gravity	Hardness, Mohs Scale
Quartz	Silica (silicon dioxide) SiO_2	2.65	7
Potash feldspar group (Orthoclase, microcline)	Aluminosilicates of potassium, also with sodium $(K,Na)Si_3O_8$ (orthoclase) $KAlSi_3O_8$ (microcline)	2.5-2.6	6
Plagioclase feldspar group	Aluminosilicates of sodium and calcium $NaAlSi_3O_8$ (albite) $CaAl_2Si_2O_8$ (anorthite)	2.62-2.76	6
Mica group (Biotite, muscovite)	Aluminosilicates of potassium, magnesium, and iron, with water (complex formulas)	2.9	2½-3
Amphibole group (Hornblende)	Silicates of aluminum, calcium, magnesium, and iron (complex formulas)	3.2	5½
Pyroxene group (Augite)	Silicates of aluminum, calcium, magnesium, and iron (complex formulas)	3.3	5½
Olivine	Silicate of magnesium and iron $(Mg,Fe)_2SiO_4$	3.3	6½-7

Figure 7.2. Two forms of quartz. (*A*) Crystals, about half natural size. (*B*) Crystalline quartz with broken surfaces. The thin, needlelike objects within the quartz are crystals of tourmaline. (Courtesy of Ward's Natural Science Establishment, Inc., Rochester, N.Y.)

agonal prism is seen only in quartz that has undergone crystal growth in open rock cavities.

The *potash feldspars* are a mineral group, of which *orthoclase* and *microcline* are abundant in certain of the igneous rocks (Figure 7.3). The word "potash" refers to the element potassium, which is the ingredient distinguishing these from other feldspars. Although commonly white or gray in color, potash feldspar may be salmon pink (or, rarely, green), giving a distinctive pink color to certain granites.

The *plagioclase feldspars* comprise a chemically related group of minerals of paramount importance in the composition of the igneous rocks. Altogether six mineral species are recognized by name in the plagioclase group, but one grades into the other in terms of proportions of the two end components—*albite*, a sodium aluminosilicate with the composition $NaAlSi_3O_8$, and *anorthite*, a calcium aluminosilicate with the composition $CaAl_2Si_2O_8$. Albite is pictured in Figure 7.4. Albite and anorthite can exist in combination in the solid crystalline state in any proportions.

The six plagioclase feldspars with proportions of the end components and percentages of sodium calcium, alumina, and silica are described in Table 7.3. The figures in this table deserve close attention, because the changes in composition from one end of the plagioclase series to the other are of fundamental importance in understanding the igneous rocks. The mineral names are of secondary importance and may be disregarded. As the series progresses from albite toward anorthite, that is to say, from the *alkalic* (*sodic*) end to the

Table 7.2. (*Continued*)

Crystal System	Cleavage or Fracture	Luster	Color
Hexagonal	No cleavage	Vitreous or greasy	Colorless and various colors
Monoclinic (orthoclase) Triclinic (microcline)	Conchoidal fracture Good prismatic cleavage at right angles	Vitreous	White, gray, or pink; also green
Triclinic	Good prismatic cleavage at 86° angle	Vitreous	White or gray
Monoclinic	Perfect cleavage in one plane	Vitreous to pearly	Black or dark brown
Monoclinic	Imperfect prismatic cleavage at 56° and 124° angles	Vitreous or silky	Dark green to black
Monoclinic	Imperfect prismatic cleavage at 87° angle	Vitreous	Dark green to black
Orthorhombic	No cleavage	Vitreous	Yellowish green to bottle green

Figure 7.3. Microcline feldspar, showing cleavage surfaces. (Courtesy of Ward's Natural Science Establishment, Inc., Rochester, N.Y.)

Figure 7.4. Albite feldspar, showing cleavage surfaces. (Courtesy of American Museum of Natural History.)

calcic end, not only do the proportions of sodium and calcium reverse position, but there are important changes in the content of aluminum (as *alumina*, Al_2O_3) and silicon (as *silica*, SiO_2). The percentage of alumina almost doubles, while the percentage of silica decreases by about one-third. We shall see in later pages that plagioclase feldspar, at the alkalic end of the series, is associated with quite different igneous rocks than those associated with the calcic end. (The term *alkali feldspars* is used to include the potash feldspars and albite, all of which contain potassium or sodium or both, but little or no calcium.)

For purposes of simplification, this list of silicate minerals does not include a group known as the *feldspathoids,* which are aluminum silicates of potassium and sodium with less silica than the feldspars. These minerals take the place of the feldspars in igneous rocks that have a deficiency of silica. One of the feldspathoid group, the mineral *nepheline,* assumes importance in one group of igneous rocks. Its formula is $NaAlSiO_4$. Notice the lower silica content (43%) as compared with the formula for albite (67%).

The *mica group* consists of silicates of aluminum, commonly with potassium, and in the case of the dark mica *biotite,* described in Table 7.2, also contains iron and magnesium. In addition, a distinctive feature of the chemical composition of the micas is the presence of small amounts of water locked into the crystal structure. In the chemical formulas of the micas the water can be represented by the *hydroxyl ion* (OH). The most striking physical feature of the micas is their perfect cleavage in one plane only.

Table 7.3. THE PLAGIOCLASE FELDSPAR GROUP

Name	Percent Albite	Percent Anorthite	Percent Sodium as Na_2O	Percent Calcium as CaO	Percent Alumina Al_2O_3	Percent Silica SiO_2
Alkalic (Sodic) Albite	100	0	11	0.0-0.8	20	67
	90	10				
Oligoclase			10	3	23	64
	70	30				
Intermediate Andesine			6	8	26	58
	50	50				
Labradorite			4	12	30	53
	30	70				
Bytownite			3	15	32	49
	10	90				
Calcic Anorthite			0.2-0.8	19	35	44
	0	100				

Source: Based on data of W. A. Deer, R. A. Howie, and J. Zussman (1966), *An Introduction to the Rock-Forming Minerals,* New York, Wiley, pp. 324-325, Table 31.

As a result, mica can be split into thin, flexible sheets (Figure 7.5*A*). Biotite is a common constituent of the igneous rocks. *Muscovite,* a pale-colored mica which appears clear in thin sheets or flakes, is also a common mica and occurs in various metamorphic rocks and in some igneous rocks (Figure 7.5*B*). Iron and magnesium are absent from the composition of muscovite, a fact that explains its light color.

The *amphibole group* consists of minerals which are silicates of aluminum, calcium, magnesium, and iron. *Hornblende* is the common variety described in Table 7.2 and is an important constituent of the igneous rocks. Notice that this mineral is relatively dense (specific gravity 3.2) and is dark in color. It has imperfect prismatic cleavage in which the planes have angles of intersection of 56° and 124°.

The *pyroxene group* is closely similar in chemical and physical properties to the amphiboles. The group includes a dozen mineral species of quite varied composition. All are silicates and contain important amounts of calcium, magnesium, and iron; some also have substantial amounts of aluminum, titanium, or sodium. The common variety *augite,* described in Table 7.2, is not easily distinguished from hornblende, but the prismatic cleavage angle of 87°, close to a right angle, can serve as a distinguishing criterion (Figure 7.6).

Olivine, treated here as a single mineral, is also one of a mineral group bearing that name.

A silicate of magnesium and iron, this greenish mineral has a simple chemical formula. Magnesium is usually present in greater proportion than iron, and in some analyses magnesium (calculated as MgO) comprises half the total content. Specific gravity of olivine is approximately the same as for pyroxene, about 3.3. Absence of any cleavage is an important physical property of olivine, contrasting with the well-developed cleavages of the amphiboles and pyroxenes.

Among the more important newly formed minerals distinctive of dynamothermal metamorphism are the following (Table 7.4): *kyanite, andalusite, staurolite,* and *garnet* (variety *almandite*). All four are aluminosilicates. As a group they are hard minerals with specific gravities comparable to those of the mafic minerals. Crystals of distinctive form grow in the metamorphic rock and are often easily recognized (Figure 7.7).

Wollastonite, a silicate of calcium, is derived from carbonate rocks by contact metamorphism. *Tremolite,* a magnesium silicate, is derived from recrystallization of dolomite. *Graphite,* consisting of carbon, comes from carbonaceous matter in sedimentary rocks.

D. ATOMIC STRUCTURE OF CRYSTALLINE MINERALS

Cleavage is an important internal physical property of many minerals. Among the silicate minerals the cleavage varies considerably: Quartz and olivine exhibit no cleavage; the feldspars and

Figure 7.6. A crystal of pyroxene, about half natural size, showing natural parting (top surface). (Courtesy of Ward's Natural Science Establishment, Inc., Rochester, N.Y.)

Figure 7.5. (*A*) Biotite mica is black, with highly lustrous cleavage surfaces. (Courtesy of Ward's Natural Science Establishment, Inc., Rochester, N.Y.) (*B*) Muscovite mica is light in color. Surfaces on the top and sides of this specimen are crystal surfaces. (Courtesy of the American Museum of Natural History.) Vertical surfaces facing the observer are cleavage planes.

pyroxenes have prismatic cleavage varying in perfection and angle; the micas have remarkably perfect cleavage in one direction only. An explanation of these differences lies in an understanding of the manner in which the component atoms, as ions, are fitted together in a crystal structure.

One of the simplest examples with which to begin is that of the mineral *halite,* or rock salt, with the formula NaCl. It has been noted that

Table 7.4. REPRESENTATIVE METAMORPHIC MINERALS

Mineral Name	Composition	Specific Gravity	Hardness, Mohs Scale	Crystal System and Habit	Color	Occurrence in Rocks
Kyanite	Aluminum silicate Al_2SiO_5	3.6	7	Triclinic system; bladed crystals	Blue, bluish gray, green, white	Schists, gneisses
Andalusite	Aluminum silicate Al_2SiO_5	3.2	7½	Orthorhombic system; prismatic crystals, nearly square	Gray, whitish	Schists, slates
Staurolite	Hydrous aluminosilicate with iron $FeAl_5(OH)(SiO_6)_2$	3.7	7-7½	Orthorhombic system; prisms, esp. penetration twins	Brown	Schists, gneisses
Garnet (var. Almandite	Aluminosilicate of iron $Fe_3Al_2(SiO_4)_3$	4.2	7	Isometric system; dodecahedrons, trapezohedrons	Deep red, brownish red	Schists, gneisses
Wollastonite	Calcium silicate $CaSiO_3$	2.8	4½-5	Triclinic system; fibrous or columnar	White or gray	Crystalline limestones
Tremolite (an amphibole)	Hydrous magnesium silicate $H_2Mg_7(SiO_3)_8$	3.1	5-6	Monoclinic system; prismatic, fibrous	White, gray, green	Crystalline dolomites and limestones, schists
Graphite	Carbon C	3.1	1-2	Hexagonal system	Dark gray, black Metallic luster Gray streak Sectile	Schists, gneisses, marbles

Figure 7.7. Garnet crystals in schist. The larger crystal is 0.8 in. (2 cm) across. (Photograph by A. N. Strahler.)

halite belongs to the isometric crystal system (Figure 7.1) and that its natural external crystal form is the cube. When halite is crushed, the cleavage is found to be excellent in three sets of perpendicular planes, yielding innumerable cleavage cubes. In this mineral, then, cleavage and external crystal form are alike, reflecting the atomic structure of the mineral (Figure 7.8).

Within a crystal structure, elements exist as *ions* or as *ionic groups* bearing either a negative or a positive electrical charge. Ions of unlike charge tend to be attracted together and to be held by *ionic bonds.* In the case of halite, the positively charged sodium ion (Na^+) is bonded to the negatively charged chlorine ion (Cl^-). Because the charges are of equal magnitude for both ions, they must be arranged in space so that each ion of a given charge is surrounded by six equidistantly spaced ions of the opposite charge. This arrangement is illustrated in Figure 7.8. If we connect the centers of the ions with straight lines, a *cubic space lattice* results (left part of Figure 7.8).

The ionic bonds in halite are not particularly strong, thus the lattice can be easily split in three sets of planes passing between the ions. Bonding is of equal strength in all three planes, hence a cubical cleavage results. The comparatively low hardness of halite (2.5) and ease of crushing are also explained by this form of atomic structure.

Notice in Figure 7.8 that the space lattice is shown in two forms. In the center diagram, ions are depicted as spheres scaled in size in proportion to the *atomic radius* of the ions they represent. In Angstrom units (see Chapter 1 in *Planet Earth*), the atomic radius of the sodium ion is 0.98, and that of the chlorine ion is 1.8. The smaller sodium ions are fitted as closely as possible among the larger chlorine ions. In the left part of Figure 7.8, the ionic arrangement has been expanded graphically and the bonds are depicted by line segments in order that the lattice can be seen.

Three other kinds of bonds exist in crystalline solids. In *van der Waal's bonding,* molecules of the compound retain their identity and are rather weakly bonded to their neighbors. An example is ice, which, as we all know, is easily crushed. *Metallic* bonding, found in malleable and ductile metals, is not applicable to the rock-forming minerals. The third kind, in which *covalent bonds* exist, is of primary importance here, since the main bonding found in the silicate minerals is partly ionic and partly covalent.

The essential building block of lattice structure of all of the silicate minerals is the *silicon-oxygen tetrahedron,* pictured in unexpanded form in Figure 7.9. It consists of four oxygen ions (O^{2-}) surrounding a single silicon ion (Si^{4+}). The expanded form of this tetrahedron is shown in Figure 7.10. In its central position, the small silicon ion fits neatly into the space between the four surrounding large oxygen ions.

Table 7.5 gives the necessary data on the

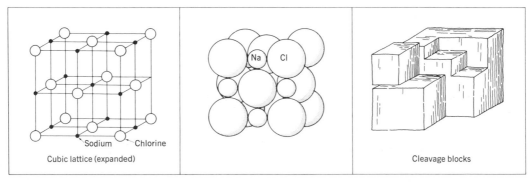

Figure 7.8. Structure of halite.

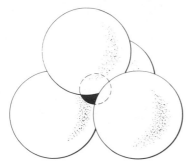

Figure 7.9. Unexpanded silicon-oxygen tetrahedron.

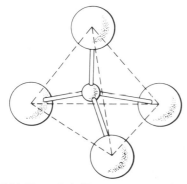

Figure 7.10. Expanded silicon-oxygen tetrahedron.

charges and ionic radii of the eight elements. Weights of single atoms are also given. Notice that the ionic radius of silicon (0.42 A) is less than one-third that of oxygen (1.40 A). This ratio of sizes is just right to enable the silicon ion to occupy the space between the four enclosing oxygen ions.

The combined unit charges of the four oxygen ions is 8⁻, whereas that of the silicon ion is 4⁺. It is obvious that, isolated by itself, the sili-

Table 7.5. IONIC RADII AND CHARGES OF THE MOST ABUNDANT ELEMENTS OF THE EARTH'S CRUST

Element	Symbol	Ionic Radius, Angstroms	Unit Charge	Weight of One Atom $\times 10^{-24}$ gm (rounded)
Oxygen	O	1.40	2−	27
Silicon	Si	0.42	4+	47
Aluminum	Al	0.51	3+	45
Iron	Fe	0.74	2+	93
		or 0.64	or 3+	
Calcium	Ca	0.99	2+	20
Sodium	Na	0.97	1+	38
Potassium	K	1.33	1+	65
Magnesium	Mg	0.66	2+	40

Source: Data from Jack Green (1953), *Bull. Geol. Soc. Amer.*, vol. 64, p. 1001, Table 3.

con-oxygen tetrahedron cannot constitute a stable compound. However, these tetrahedrons can be arranged in such a way that all charges are balanced, which case is represented by quartz.

The lattice structure of quartz is illustrated in Figure 7.11. The tetrahedra are so arranged

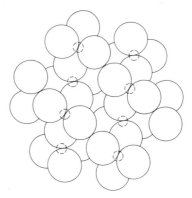

Figure 7.11. Arrangement of tetrahedra in a quartz crystal.

that each oxygen ion is common to two tetrahedra, in other words, that the oxygen ions are *shared*. In effect, the one silicon ion within the tetrahedron is equated to only four units of negative charge. In this way the charges are balanced and a stable compound is produced. Because the ionic bonds are equally strong in all directions, no planes of weakness exist in the structure of quartz, and it exhibits no cleavage.

We turn next to the last mineral on the list, olivine, to illustrate a different arrangement of silicon-oxygen tetrahedra, which, together with other ions, are so arranged as to produce strong bonding in all directions. Figure 7.12 shows the lattice structure of olivine. In the top view, tetrahedra are equidistantly separated and the intermediate positions are occupied by ions of iron or magnesium. The formula for olivine is $(Mg,Fe)_2SiO_4$. Both iron and magnesium ions have two positive unit charges each, so that within the compound the eight negative charges of oxygen are balanced by the total of eight positive charges. In the lattice structure this balance is achieved by an arrangement in which alternate layers of tetrahedra are inverted (upside down), the points thus fitting into space between the opposed tetrahedra, as shown in the upper part of Figure 7.12, with ions of either magnesium or iron occupying spaces intermediate between the tetrahedra. Thus linked to the oxygen ions, an ion of magnesium or iron shares the double unit charge of each oxygen ion with the silicon ion inside the tetrahedron. The lattice structure of

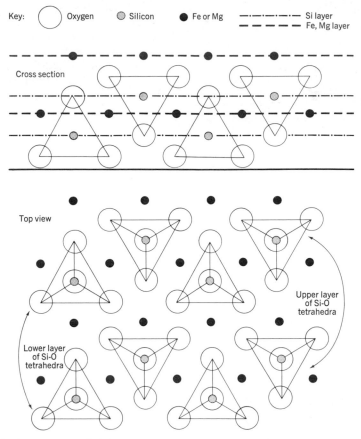

Figure 7.12. Crystal lattice structure of olivine.

olivine lacks planes of weakness, and consequently there is no cleavage.

Lattice structures of the other silicate minerals are more complex and are treated here in more generalized descriptions. The structures can consist of either *chains* or *sheets*. A single chain of tetrahedra, linked by their shared oxygen ions, is the basic arrangement of the pyroxenes (augite), as shown in Figure 7.13. Adjacent chains are linked by ions of magnesium, iron,

Figure 7.13. Single chain of silicon-oxygen tetrahedra.

calcium, or aluminum. The arrangement is such that two planes of weaker bonding exist at about right angles ($87°$), giving the prismatic cleavage seen in augite.

A double chain of silicon-oxygen tetrahedra characterizes the amphiboles (hornblende), as shown in Figure 7.14. In this arrangement the tetrahedra alternately share two and three oxygen ions. Ions of magnesium, iron, calcium, sodium, or potassium occupy positions between chains. This arrangement results in two directions of weaker bonding and yields two sets of cleavage planes at angles of $56°$ and $124°$, as seen in hornblende.

The micas possess an interesting sheet structure, pictured in Figure 7.15. The silicon-oxygen tetrahedra are arranged in sheets in which each of the three basal oxygen ions is shared with an adjacent tetrahedron. A single layer, seen from above the plane of the sheet, forms a pattern of hexagonal cells. Alternate sheets of tetrahedra are inverted, as seen in the side view of Figure 7.15. Sheets are alternately separated by layers of positively charged ions, but these intervening

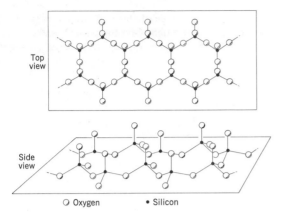

Top view

Side view

○ Oxygen   • Silicon

Figure 7.14. Perspective drawings of a double chain of tetrahedra in the structure of amphibole. [From *General Crystallography: A Brief Compendium* by W. F. de Jong. W. H. Freeman and Company. Copyright © 1959.]

layers alternate in composition. Between those pairs of sheets in which the tetrahedra points

are opposed lies a layer of magnesium ions, forming a strong bonding between sheets. Hydroxyl ions (OH) occupy spaces in the plane of the tetrahedron points. Between those pairs of sheets in which the bases of the tetrahedra are opposed there is a layer of potassium ions. Here the van der Waal's bonds are weak, forming a natural set of parallel parting planes. This sheet structure explains the remarkably perfect cleavage of biotite and muscovite micas in a single set of parallel planes.

The feldspars present a still different structural arrangement of silicon-oxygen tetrahedra. In a framework somewhat similar to that of quartz, the tetrahedra are linked in a continuous network in which all oxygen ions are shared. The principal difference is that in the feldspars a certain proportion of the silicon ions has been replaced with aluminum ions (three positive units of charge). There is thus a net nega-

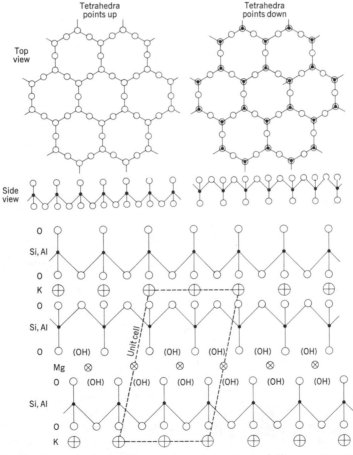

Figure 7.15. Crystal lattice structure of mica. Upper diagram shows sheets of silicon-oxygen tetrahedra. Lower diagram is a cross section through three sheets of tetrahedra with intervening layers of potassium and magnesium ions. [Modified from W. A. Deer, R. A. Howie, and J. Zussman (1966), *An Introduction to the Rock-Forming Minerals*, London, Longman Group Ltd., pp. 194-195, Figures 69, 71.]

tive charge, resulting from the replacement, and this is equalized by ions of sodium, potassium, or calcium, which are distributed through the network. Because certain sets of bonds are weaker than others, cleavage is developed in two intersecting sets of planes.

E. IGNEOUS ROCK TEXTURES

While mineral composition constitutes the first basis of igneous rock classification, the second basis of classification is *textural* and relates to the sizes of the component mineral crystals and to the patterns of arrangements of those crystals. Texture also encompasses the noncrystalline state.

Among the crystalline igneous rocks texture falls into two classes: (1) *Phaneritic texture* consists of crystals large enough to be seen with the unaided eye or with the help of a small hand lens (see Figure 7.6 in *Planet Earth*). (2) *Aphanitic texture* consists of crystals too small to be distinguished as individual particles without the aid of the microscope. Where all crystals in the rock are about of the same size range, the texture is described as *equigranular*. Quite different is the case where a few large crystals, called *phenocrysts,* are embedded in a coarse- or fine-grained or glassy matrix, or *groundmass.* Such texture is *porphyritic* and the rock is designated as a *porphyry* in addition to its proper name (Figure 7.16).

The crystalline fabric of the phaneritic rocks is best studied under a specialized microscope in which very thin slices of the rock are examined under transmitted light (see Figure 7.7 in *Planet Earth*). For the most part, external crystal forms are lacking or only poorly developed. On the other hand, evidences of cleavage show up well as linear markings within the grains. The use of polarized light makes possible mineral identification based upon distinctive optical properties. This branch of petrology is known as *petrography.*

The phaneritic igneous rocks with equigranular textures have crystal grains ranging in diameter from 0.002 in. (0.05 mm) to over 0.4 in. (10 mm). An accepted grade scale is as follows:

Fine-grained	0.002-0.04 in. (0.05-1 mm)
Medium-grained	0.04-0.2 in. (1-5 mm)
Coarse-grained	0.2-0.4 in. (5-10 mm)
Pegmatitic texture	0.4 in.-1 ft (10 mm-0.3 m)

Particles under 0.002 in. (0.05 mm) are too small to be separated by the unaided eye and fall into the amphanitic texture class. A few enormous crystals found in pegmatites run to many feet in length, with a maximum known length of over 30 ft (6 m).

The extrusive igneous rocks have distinctive textures resulting from the rapid expansion of volatile gases as confining pressure is reduced and cooling occurs. The specimen of volcanic *scoria* shown in Figure 7.17 is full of cavities

Figure 7.17. Scoria (*left*); volcanic glass, or obsidian (*right*). (Photograph by A. N. Strahler.)

formed by gas bubbles, and this texture is described as *scoriaceous.* In contrast, the *volcanic glass* (or *obsidian*), also pictured in Figure 7.17, is dense and free of such cavities. Notice the conchoidal fracture of the obsidian. In an extreme case of scoriaceous texture, the magma is frothed by expanding gases to solidify into a rock of very low density known as *pumice.*

Figure 7.16. This andesite porphyry has large feldspar phenocrysts scattered through an aphanitic ground mass. Specimen is 3 in. (7.6 cm) wide. (Photograph by A. N. Strahler.)

F. THE GRANITE-GABBRO SERIES

Figure 7.18 organizes the more common varieties of the igneous rocks into an orderly classification based upon mineral composition. The graph is partly quantitative in that percentages by volume of the component minerals or mineral groups are suggested by a set of numbers for each named rock variety. It is particularly important to be aware that the numbers given here are to serve only as approximate guide values. The continuous curved boundary lines on the field of the graph suggest the manner in which one rock variety can grade into the next. Consequently the assigned rock name can apply to transitional zones between it and the adjacent varieties. Two sets of rock names are given. One set applies to the intrusive plutonic rock bodies, usually of medium to coarse crystal grain texture, and the second set applies to the extrusive rocks, largely lavas. Lavas are typically aphanitic or glassy and often scoriaceous in texture.

Principal rocks of this series are described in Chapter 7 of *Planet Earth.* Not mentioned are two relatively less important rocks, *granodiorite* and *tonalite,* including their extrusive equivalents *quartz latite* and *dacite,* respectively. Note that for these rocks potash feldspar and quartz decrease in proportion, while plagioclase feldspar increases and moves from the alkalic end toward the intermediate varieties.

Figure 7.18 shows the igneous rock series extended beyond granite in the direction of the felsic minerals. In this part of the graph we find a group of rocks of considerable interest scientifically, despite their relatively limited or rare occurrence. *Quartz syenite* and its extrusive equivalent, *trachyte,* are dominated by potash feldspar and contain relatively minor amounts of quartz, plagioclase feldspar, biotite, and hornblende. As the syenite series is extended further, quartz disappears entirely and its place is taken by *nepheline* or other feldspathoid minerals. This composition results from a deficiency of silica in the magma. Quartz and nepheline cannot be found together in the same igneous rock, and this is shown in the arrangement of boundary curves in Figure 7.18. The extreme end of

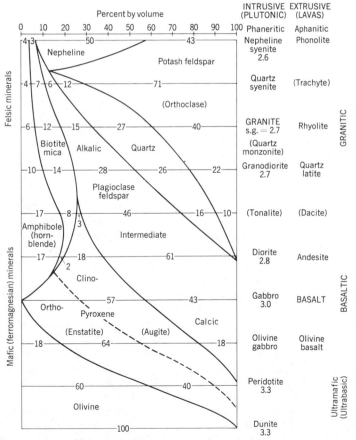

Figure 7.18. Mineral compositions of igneous rocks.

the syenite series is represented by *nepheline syenite* and its extrusive equivalent, *phonolite.* The syenite rocks are light-colored and of relatively low specific gravity, around 2.6.

Figure 7.19 is a triangular diagram of mono-

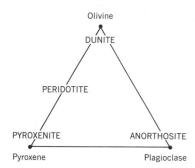

Figure 7.19. The ultramafic (ultrabasic) rocks.

mineralic ultramafic rocks referred to in Chapter 7 of *Planet Earth. Dunite,* composed largely of olivine, and *pyroxenite,* composed largely of pyroxene, are relatively rare rocks. Peridotite appears in this diagram, intermediate between dunite and pyroxenite. *Anorthosite,* composed mostly of intermediate or calcic plagioclase, usually occurs in very large masses. Although dunite, peridotite, and pyroxenite are of high specific gravity, 3.3, anorthosite has both a lower specific gravity, 2.7, typical of the granitic rocks, and a light color as well. In these respects, anorthosite is quite unlike the other three ultramafic rocks.

G. FORMS OF INTRUSIVE ROCK BODIES

Intrusive rock bodies assume a wide range of sizes and shapes. The larger masses, referred to as *plutons,* consist of rock of phaneritic texture, usually of medium- to coarse-grained crystal sizes. A large variety of smaller instrusive bodies are fine-grained or aphanitic in texture because of rapid cooling in contact with surrounding rock.

Largest of the plutonic bodies is the *batholith* (Figure 7.20), usually of granitic rock composition, but in certain cases consisting of anorthosite. A single batholith may have an areal extent of several thousand square miles. An example is the Idaho batholith, of which 16,000 mi^2 (40,000 km^2) is exposed, equal to the combined areas of New Hampshire and Vermont. Another example is the Sierra Nevada batholith of California, underlying much of the Sierra Nevada range (see Figure 7.12 in *Planet Earth*).

As a batholith is uncovered, there appear

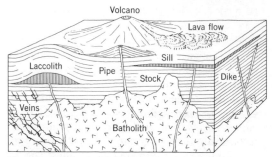

Figure 7.20. Forms of occurrence of the igneous rocks. (© 1960, John Wiley & Sons, New York.)

first smaller bodies of the plutonic rock known as *stocks,* which occupy areas of less than 40 mi^2 (100 km^2) (Figure 7.20). Remnants of the *country rock* (rock into which the igneous rock was intruded) will be found extending down into the batholith as *roof pendants.*

Figure 7.20 shows other forms of intrusive rock bodies. The country rock is depicted as having a layered structure, as would be the case for sedimentary strata. Magma intruding these layers may spread out into a thin sheet of relatively great horizontal extent named a *sill.* Where magma pressure lifts the overlying layers into a dome, a *laccolith* results. In thick sills and large laccoliths the rock texture is that of a pluton.

Fractures in previously formed solid rock may be invaded by magma, which forces the enclosing rock mass apart, resulting in more-or-less vertical *dikes,* wall-like igneous rock bodies. Dikes are typically of small thickness—from a few inches to a few yards—and have a fine-grained crystalline texture. Shrinkage in cooling of thin sills and dikes results in a system of joint fractures that produces long rock columns of prismatic form with four, five, or six sides. This structure is termed *columnar jointing.* The columns are oriented with the long dimension at right angles to the enclosing country-rock surfaces. Consequently columns are typically vertical in orientation in sills and horizontal in dikes.

Watery silica-rich solutions that remain after a magma has largely crystallized are forced to penetrate fractures in either the newly formed igneous body or the adjacent country rock. Minerals deposited from such solutions take the form of *veins* (Figure 7.20). One important class of veins consists of *pegmatite,* described in Chapter 7 of *Planet Earth* as having a rock texture of unusually large crystals. Other types of veins contain concentrations of uncommon minerals, among them the ores of various metals.

BANK 8
MINERALS FOUND IN SEDIMENTS

A. ALTERATION PRODUCTS OF SILICATE MINERALS

Table 8.1 shows examples of the alteration products of several silicate minerals or mineral groups. A simple example of hydrolysis is seen in the change of potash feldspar of the microcline variety into the clay mineral *kaolinite*. In kaolinite the union with water is represented by the hydroxyl ion (OH). Notice that kaolinite does not contain potassium, present in the original feldspar. The potassium is released as a free positive ion in the soil water or is used by plants. In the alteration of feldspar to kaolinite, free silica

(SiO_2) is also released and may remain in solution. Kaolinite is a soft white mineral with a greasy feel. It becomes plastic and exudes a distinctive "clay" odor when moistened. Kaolinite is an important ceramic material used in the manufacture of chinaware, porcelain, and tile. Under the electron microscope kaolinite proves to be composed of small tabular crystals (Figure 8.1), which possess a sheet structure very much

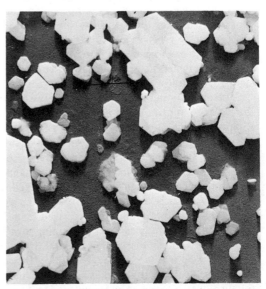

Figure 8.1. Electron microscope photograph of kaolinite crystals, magnified about 20,000 times. (Photograph by Paul F. Kerr.)

like that of muscovite mica. Muscovite with the formula $KAl_3Si_3O_{10}(OH)_2$ differs from kaolinite principally in the inclusion of potassium. Muscovite can, in fact, be formed by the hydrolysis of potash feldspar and in turn can be converted to kaolinite by the loss of the potassium ion. Hydrolysis of the sodic plagioclase feldspar can also yield kaolinite and free silica (Table 8.1).

Table 8.1. ALTERATION PRODUCTS OF SILICATE MINERALS

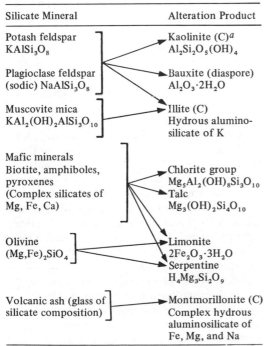

Silicate Mineral	Alteration Product
Potash feldspar $KAlSi_3O_8$	Kaolinite (C)[a] $Al_2Si_2O_5(OH)_4$
Plagioclase feldspar (sodic) $NaAlSi_3O_8$	Bauxite (diaspore) $Al_2O_3 \cdot 2H_2O$
Muscovite mica $KAl_2(OH)_2AlSi_3O_{10}$	Illite (C) Hydrous aluminosilicate of K
Mafic minerals Biotite, amphiboles, pyroxenes (Complex silicates of Mg, Fe, Ca)	Chlorite group $Mg_5Al_2(OH)_8Si_3O_{10}$ Talc $Mg_3(OH)_2Si_4O_{10}$
Olivine $(Mg,Fe)_2SiO_4$	Limonite $2Fe_2O_3 \cdot 3H_2O$ Serpentine $H_4Mg_3Si_2O_9$
Volcanic ash (glass of silicate composition)	Montmorillonite (C) Complex hydrous aluminosilicate of Fe, Mg, and Na

[a]Letter "C" denotes a clay mineral.

Under conditions of prevailingly warm and wet environments such as are found in equatorial and tropical wet-dry climate zones, alteration of the feldspars leads to formation of *bauxite*, composed of sesquioxide of aluminum (Al_2O_3) and water (Table 8.1). Union of aluminum with oxygen represents the process of oxidation accompanying hydrolysis. Bauxite is not actually a single mineral, but probably consists of several related clay minerals (principally *diaspore*) and is usually contaminated with iron oxide and silica. Bauxite is claylike in appearance and typically has small spherical structures. Where it has accumulated in large quantities it is an important ore of aluminum.

Illite, a very abundant clay mineral in sedimentary rocks, is derived through the alteration of feldspars and also from muscovite mica, which it closely resembles in crystal lattice structure. A hydrous aluminosilicate of potassium, illite occurs as a soft, claylike substance mixed with other clay minerals (see Figure 8.6 in *Planet Earth*).

Through hydrolysis the mafic minerals can yield *chlorite* and *talc*. Both are hydrous magnesium silicates. They are soft, scaly substances usually grayish to greenish in color. Talc is familiar to most persons for its soapy or greasy feel ("talcum powder") and was widely used in cut slabs for laboratory table tops and sink tops.

The mafic minerals also normally release iron during decomposition and this oxidizes to take the form of the mineral *limonite,* a hydrous sesquioxide of iron (Table 8.1). An earthy substance largely noncrystalline in structure, in color limonite is usually brown to yellow-brown and sometimes black. It yields a characteristic yellowish-brown streak when rubbed across an unglazed porcelain plate. Limonite can be derived from the weathering of any mineral containing iron and is a very widely distributed mineral. It has served as a poor-grade iron ore (bog ore). It is closely associated with bauxite in the soil and regolith of the warm, humid equatorial and tropical climates. Both bauxite and limonite are almost immune to further chemical change under conditions of a warm, wet climate. Limonite gives a typical chocolate-brown to red color to soils of those climates and is conspicuous also as a coloring agent in rocks and soils exposed in dry regions.

Olivine, along with pyroxenes and amphiboles, is commonly altered by hydrolysis into *serpentine,* a hydrous magnesium silicate (Table 8.1). A soft, greenish mineral with greasy feel, serpentine is commonly massive in structure without apparent crystal form. A fibrous variety, one of the forms of *asbestos*, consists of delicate flexible crystal fibers which can be easily separated and can be woven into fabric (Figure 8.2).

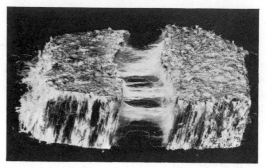

Figure 8.2. Specimen of asbestos variety of the mineral serpentine. (Photograph by courtesy of Ward's Natural Science Establishment, Rochester, N.Y.)

One of the most important clay minerals produced by alteration of igneous rock is *montmorillonite,* actually a group of related minerals. This complex hydrous aluminosilicate of iron, magnesium, and sodium is produced by the alteration of feldspar, some mafic minerals, and volcanic ash, which itself consists of shards of glass of silicate composition. Montmorillonite is soft and claylike, without any crystal form evident to the naked eye (see Figure 8.6 in *Planet Earth*).

Note that of the alteration products named here, only three are classed as clay minerals: kaolinite, illite, and montmorillonite. Clay minerals are those that give a plastic property to earth materials composed of particles of clay size and have a sheet or layered atomic structure.

Susceptibility to alteration follows the order of crystallization of the Bowen reaction series (see Figure 7.4 in *Planet Earth*). Olivine and calcic feldspar are the most easily altered, followed by the pyroxenes, amphiboles, biotite, and sodic plagioclase feldspar. Potash feldspars are generally, although not always, less susceptible than the last group, and muscovite is comparatively resistant to alteration. Quartz is in a class by itself and almost immune to chemical change beyond direct solution in water. An explanation of the relationship between mineral susceptibility to alteration and the order of crystallization is found in the environment of mineral crystallization. Olivine and calcic plagioclase were crystalized at the highest temperatures and pressures, and consequently the environment of their formation is the farthest removed with respect to atmospheric conditions.

Muscovite, crystallized at the lowest temperature and pressure, stands the least removed from atmospheric conditions.

B. THE HEAVY DETRITAL MINERALS

Table 8.2 compares quartz with four heavy detrital minerals in terms of specific gravity (relative density) and hardness.

Magnetite, an oxide of iron, is a dense mineral of iron black color and submetallic luster. It crystallizes in the isometric system and typically displays the octahedral crystal form (see Figure 8.15 in *Planet Earth*). Magnetite is strongly attracted to a magnet, thus a magnet dragged through dark-colored sands of beach or stream bed will usually emerge with a coating of magnetite grains.

Ilmenite, an oxide of iron and titanium, resembles magnetite in outward appearance but is only slightly magnetic. It is a common associate of magnetite in black beach sands. *Zircon,* a silicate of zirconium, is even harder than quartz and has a density comparable to that of magnetite. Unlike the dark metallic minerals magnetite and ilmenite, zircon can be transparent and of pale color. A highly durable mineral, zircon is important in providing a means of radiometric age determination, explained in Chapter 10 in *Planet Earth.* Minerals of the *garnet group*—aluminosilicates of calcium, magnesium, manganese, or iron—are abundant in the metamorphic rocks but also occur in igneous rocks. (A description of garnet will be found in Data Bank 7, section C, and Table 7.4 (see also Figure 7.7). Although not as dense as the three detrital heavy minerals named above, garnet is a durable mineral and will be found in company with those minerals in the dark sands of beaches and stream beds.

C. THE WENTWORTH SCALE OF SIZE GRADES

The complete Wentworth scale of grade sizes is given in Table 8.3. Units of length are milli-

meters and, for the finer grades, microns. English units are given for comparison only. In scanning down the list of numbers forming the limits of the successive classes, it is immediately evident that each number is half the value of that which precedes it and twice the value of the number that follows it. The Wentworth scale is therefore a *constant-ratio scale,* or *logarithmic scale.* One can assign an integer series of numbers to the grade class limits, as indicated in the right-hand column, labeled *phi units.* Numbers on the *phi scale* give the negative logarithm to the base 2 of the millimeter values in the first column.

In the study of sediments and sedimentary rocks, the size grades of the component particles coarser than silt are determined by the use of sieves, the openings of the sieve mesh being spaced according to the Wentworth scale. Particles that pass through a given sieve opening but are caught upon the sieve of the next smaller mesh are referred to the named size grade given in the table. The sizes of gravel particles are generally determined by direct measurement, whereas silt and clay particle sizes are determined indirectly by the rate at which they settle in a still column of water.

D. HYDROGENIC AND BIOGENIC MINERALS

Table 8.4 gives the composition and properties of eight important hydrogenic and biogenic minerals. *Calcite* is a soft mineral, easily scratched with the point of a knife. It is most easily recognized in large crystals by the excellent cleavage in three directions, forming rhombohedrons. (See Figure 8.19 in *Planet Earth.*.) Many common forms of calcite, especially in the sedimentary rocks, show no identifiable crystalline structure to the unaided eye. Application of a drop of dilute hydrochloric acid to the mineral surface results in strong effervescence (frothing) and is a standard test for the presence of calcite.

Of the same composition as calcite but much less abundant is *aragonite,* found in certain invertebrate shells. It makes up the pearly material of the shell. Aragonite is a harder mineral than calcite and lacks the good cleavage of calcite.

Dolomite, a close relative of calcite, is a carbonate of both calcium and magnesium. Denser and harder than calcite, dolomite effervesces with dilute hydrochloric acid only when in the powdered form. Like calcite, dolomite has excellent rhombohedral cleavage. In the compact

Table 8.2. HEAVY DETRITAL MINERALS
COMPARED TO QUARTZ

Mineral	Composition	Specific Gravity	Hardness
Quartz	SiO_2	2.65	7
Magnetite	$Fe(FeO_2)_2$, also Fe_3O_4	4.9-5.2	5.5-6.5
Ilmenite	$FeTiO_3$	4.3-5.5	5-6
Zircon	$ZrSiO_4$	4.4-4.8	7.5
Garnet group	Aluminosilicate of Ca, Mg, Mn, Fe	3.4-4.3	6.5-7.5

Table 8.3. THE WENTWORTH SCALE OF SIZE GRADES

Grade Name		mm	in.	Phi units
		4096	160	−12
	Very large			
		2048	80	−11
	Large			
Boulders		1024	40	−10
	Medium			
		512	20	−9
	Small			
		256	10	−8
	Large			
Cobbles		128	5	−7
	Small			
		64	2.5	−6
	Very coarse			
		32	1.3	−5
	Coarse			
		16	0.6	−4
Pebbles	Medium			
		8	0.3	−3
	Fine			
		4	0.16	−2
	Very fine			
		2	0.08	−1
	Very coarse		Microns	
		1	1000	0
	Coarse			
		0.5	500	+1
Sand	Medium			
		0.25	250	+2
	Fine			
		0.125	125	+3
	Very fine			
		0.0625	62	+4
	Coarse			
		0.0312	31	+5
Silt	Medium			
		0.016	16	+6
	Fine			
		0.008	8	+7
	Very fine			
		0.004	4	+8
	Coarse			
		0.002	2	+9
	Medium			
Clay		0.001	1	+10
	Fine			
		0.0005	0.5	+11
	Very fine			
		0.00024	0.24	+12
	(Colloids down to 0.001 microns)			

form found in rocks, particles with crystal faces are rare.

Sulfate compounds are also important as minerals of the hydrogenic sediments. *Anhydrite,* calcium sulfate, is a fairly soft mineral. It is commonly found in a granular state that gives a sugary appearance to broken surfaces. Derived directly from anhydrite by union with water (hydrolysis) is the mineral *gypsum,* a hydrous calcium sulfate. It can also be precipitated directly from solution. Gypsum is one of the softest of common minerals and defines hardness number 2 on the Mohs scale. It can be scratched with the fingernail. Gypsum has a low

Table 8.4. IMPORTANT HYDROGENIC AND BIOGENIC MINERALS

	Mineral Name	Composition	Specific Gravity	Hardness, Mohs Scale	Crystal System
Carbonates	Calcite	Calcium carbonate $CaCO_3$	2.72	3	Hexagonal
	Aragonite	Calcium carbonate $CaCO_3$	2.9-3	3.5-4	Orthorhombic
	Dolomite	Calcium-magnesium carbonate $CaMg(CO_3)_2$	2.9	2.5-4	Hexagonal
Evaporites	Anhydrite	Calcium sulfate $CaSO_4$	2.7-3	3-3.5	Orthorhombic
	Gypsum	Hydrous calcium sulfate $CaSO_4 \cdot 2H_2O$	2	2.2-2.4	Monoclinic
	Halite	Sodium chloride $NaCl$	2.1-2.3	2-2.5	Cubic
	Hematite	Sesquioxide of iron (ferric) Fe_2O_3	4.9-5.3	5.5-6.5	Hexagonal
	Chalcedony (chert, flint)	Silica SiO_2	2.6	7	Hexagonal

specific gravity, 2.2 to 2.4, and is typically fibrous in appearance, often with a silky luster.

Halite, or rock salt, was described in Data Bank 7, section D (see Figure 7.8). We are all familiar with the properties of halite, which in the refined pure form constitutes common table salt. Ease of solubility in water is the most obvious property of halite, which belongs to a class of minerals known as *evaporites.* Along with certain other highly soluble salts, halite is deposited from ocean water and the water of salt lakes when evaporation is sustained under aridity of climate. Halite has been widely produced commercially by evaporation of sea water, but by far the greatest deposits are in rock strata.

Hematite, a sesquioxide of iron (Fe_2O_3), is widespread in certain sequences of sedimentary strata. Notice that hematite represents the *ferric* form of iron oxide, as distinct from the *ferrous oxide* (FeO) found in magnetite. (The composition of magnetite, often given as Fe_3O_4, can be also written as $FeO \cdot Fe_2O_3$, a combination of ferrous and ferric oxides.) In terms of sediments and sedimentary rocks, this distinction is important because hematite contains the greater proportion of oxygen, a consequence of exposure to free oxygen of the atmosphere. Hematite occurs in many forms and is particularly important as a sedimentary form of iron ore.

E. PROPERTIES OF REPRESENTATIVE ORE MINERALS

Metal	Symbol	Mineral Name	Composition	Hardness	S.G.	Streak	Luster	Color	Form and Other Properties
Aluminum	Al	Bauxite (not a single mineral)	Hydrous aluminum oxide (Complex) (35-40% Al)	Varies (soft)	Varies		Dull to earthy	White, when pure; brown, yellow	Amorphous. Earthy masses; claylike. Pisolitic structure common.
Iron	Fe	Magnetite	$Fe(FeO_2)_2$ (72.4% Fe)	6	5.1	Black	Metallic	Black	Crystalline, in granular masses. Octahedral crystals. Strongly attracted to magnet.
		Hematite	Fe_2O_3 (70.0% Fe)	6	5.2	Brownish red	Metallic to dull	Iron black to dark red	Finely crystalline to massive and earthy.
		Limonite (not a single mineral)	$Fe_2O \cdot nH_2O$ (50-60% Fe)	5½	3.8	Yellow-brown	Dull to submetallic	Yellow, brown, or black	Earthy; compact masses.
		Pyrite	FeS_2 (46.6% Fe)	6-6½	5	Greenish to brownish-black	Metallic	Pale brass yellow	Commonly crystalline: cube, octahedron, pyritohedron, with striated faces.
Magnesium	Mg	(From MgCl in brines)							
Titanium	Ti	Rutile	TiO_2 (60% Ti)	6-6½	4.2	Pale brown	Metallic to adamantine	Red, brownish red, black	Crystalline. Prismatic or columnar crystals (tetragonal).
		Ilmenite	$FeTiO_3$ (31.6% Ti)	5-6	4.7	Black to brownish red	Submetallic to metallic	Black	Crystalline. Tabular or rhombohedral crystals (hexagonal). No cleavage.
Manganese	Mn	Pyrolusite	MnO_2 (with some water) (30% Mn)	1-2½	4.8	Black	Metallic to dull	Black	Amorphous. Fibrous, massive, or in crusts.
		Manganite	$Mn_2O_3 \cdot H_2O$	4	4.3	Dark brown	Submetallic	Iron black	Prismatic crystals (orthorhombic); fibrous masses.
Vanadium	V	(See carnotite)							
Chromium	Cr	Chromite	$FeCr_2O_4$ (with variable Al, Mg, Fe)	5½	4.4	Dark brown	Submetallic or metallic	Black	Disseminated, or as compact masses.
Nickel	Ni	Pentlandite	$(Fe,Ni)S$ (20-40% Ni)	3½-4	4.8	Light bronze brown	Metallic	Bronze yellow	Massive; resembles pyrrhotite.

Element	Symbol	Mineral	Formula	% Metal	Hardness	G	Streak	Luster	Color	Crystal form / Remarks
Zinc	Zn	Sphalerite	(Zn,Fe)S	(67% Zn)	3½–4	4.0	Pale yellow to dark brown	Adamantine to submetallic	Pale yellow, yellowish brown, or reddish brown	Crystalline. Tetrahedrons (cubic). Prominent cleavage.
Copper	Cu	Native copper	Cu		2½	8.8		Metallic	Copper red	Grains, sheets, wires. Malleable.
		Chalcopyrite	$CuFeS_2$	(34.5% Cu)	3½–4	4.2	Greenish black	Metallic	Brass yellow; iridescent tarnish	Massive or disseminated.
		Chalcocite	Cu_2S	(80% Cu)	2½	5.8	Dark gray	Metallic	Lead gray, dull black with tarnish	Compact; fine-grained masses.
Cobalt	Co	Cobaltite	CoAsS	(35.4% Co)	5½	6	Grayish black	Metallic	Silvery white, reddish tinge	Crystals resembling pyrite. Also granular or massive.
Lead	Pb	Galena	PbS	(86.6% Pb)	2½	7.5	Silvery gray to grayish black	Metallic	Silver-gray	Crystalline (cubes, octahedrons). Perfect cubic cleavage, also granular or massive.
Tin	Sn	Cassiterite	SnO_2	(78.6 Sn)	6½	7.0		Adamantine	Brown to black	Crystals (tetragonal), or as pebbles and sand grains.
Molybdenum	Mo	Molybdenite	MoS_2	(60% Mo)	1½	4.7	Greenish	Metallic	Bluish gray	Scales or masses. Cleavage perfect in one direction. Sectile.
Tungsten	W	Wolframite	$(Fe,Mn)WO_4$		5–5½	7.4		Submetallic	Black, dark brown	Crystalline aggregates. Cleavage perfect in one direction.
Uranium	U	Pitchblende (uraninite)	Hydrous uranium oxide		5½	6.5–8	Olive green	Submetallic or pitchlike	Dark brown to black	Amorphous. Massive. (Uraninite is crystalline form.)
		Carnotite	Hydrous oxides of potassium, vanadium, and uranium		(soft)	4.1		Resinous to dull	Canary yellow	Amorphous; earthy masses or encrustations.
Antimony	Sb	Stibnite	Sb_2S_3	(71.4% Sb)	2	4.5	Lead gray	Brilliant metallic	Lead gray	Crystal aggregates; bladed or prismatic (orthorhombic).
Mercury	Hg	Cinnabar	HgS	(86.2% Hg)	2½	8.0	Vermilion	Adamantine	Scarlet to dark red	Disseminated, or massive, earthy.

E. PROPERTIES OF REPRESENTATIVE ORE MINERALS (*Continued*)

Metal	Symbol	Mineral Name	Composition	Hardness	S.G.	Streak	Luster	Color	Form and Other Properties
Silver	Ag	Native silver	Ag	2½	10.5		Metallic	Tin white to pale yellow (tarnished)	Malleable. Wires, sheets, branched forms.
		Argentite	Ag_2S (87.1% Ag)	2½	7.3		Metallic	Dark lead gray	Massive; as crusts. Sectile.
Gold	Au	Native gold	Au,Ag	2½-3	15-19		Metallic	Deep yellow to pale yellow	Disseminated; or as scales, grains, or nuggets. Malleable.
Platinum	Pt	Platinum	Pt (alloyed with Fe and other metals)	4½	15-19		Metallic	Light steel gray	Grains, scales, lumps, nuggets. Malleable.

BANK 9

TOPOGRAPHIC AND
GEOLOGIC MAPS

A. CONTOUR MAPS AND OTHER ISOPLETH MAPS

In almost every branch of the earth sciences it is necessary to show the distribution of some physical property over an area of the earth's sea-level datum or at some given level above or below that surface. Such maps consist of lines connecting all points having the same quantity or value. The lines are in general referred to as *isopleths* (from the Greek *isos,* equal, and *plēthos,* fullness or quantity), and the maps are known as *isopleth maps.* The term *isarithm* (from the Greek *arithmos,* number) is also used in scientific writing in essentially the same sense as isopleth.

The technique of constructing, reading, and interpreting isopleth maps may be illustrated by study of the *topographic contour map,* familiar to many persons because of its widespread use to depict the relief features of the landscape. (*Topography* means the configuration of the ground surface.) A *contour line* is a line drawn on the map through all points having equal elevation above a *datum,* usually mean sea level (Figure 9.1). A contour line is therefore an *isohypse* (from the Greek *hypso,* height), but this term is little used in English writing. Table

9.1 lists a variety of isopleths encountered in various branches of the earth sciences. Examples are found in the text of *Planet Earth.*

A most important property of isopleth maps is that the relative horizontal spacing of successive isopleths indicates the *gradient,* or rate at which the value is changing with respect to horizontal distance. In the example of the island (Figure 9.1) the gradient of the ground surface is steep on the right-hand side, hence the contours are closely spaced in descending from *B* to *A.* By contrast, the ground slope from *B* down to *C* is gentle, hence the contours there are spaced widely apart.

If in the case of the island shown in Figure 9.1 the sea level were to rise exactly 10 ft, the water would come to rest on the line of the 10-ft contour line, a second rise of 10 more ft

Table 9.1. EXAMPLES OF ISOPLETHS

Name of Isopleth	Greek Root	Property Described	Examples in Text[a]
Isobar	*baros,* weight	Barometric pressure	*PE* 4.3, 4.17
Isotherm	*therme,* heat	Temperature of air, water, or soil	4.13, 4.15
Isotach	*tachos,* swift	Fluid velocity	*PE* 4.20
Isohyet	*hyetos,* rain	Precipitation	*PE* 6.11, 5.7
Isohypse	*hypso,* height	Elevation	9.4
Isopach	*pachys,* thick	Thickness, as of a rock stratum, or glacial ice	*PE* 6.21
Isobath	*bathos,* depth	Depth, of water	
Isocline	*clino,* slope	Magnetic dip	*PE* 2.13
Isogonic line, or isogone	*gonia,* angle	Magnetic declination	*PE* 2.16
Isodyne	*dynamis,* power	Magnetic intensity	*PE* 2.14

[a] *"PE"* denotes figures found in *Planet Earth.*

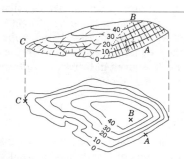

Figure 9.1. Principle of the topographic contour map. (© 1960, John Wiley & Sons, New York.)

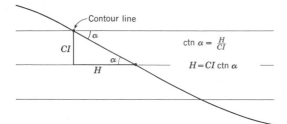

Figure 9.2. Relation of contour spacing to surface gradient.

would bring the water line to the 20-ft contour line, etc. Successive contour lines have a constant unit of vertical separation, the *contour interval.*

To be exact about the relation of gradient to spacing of isopleths, refer to Figure 9.2. The angle of surface slope, or gradient, is represented by the angle α, which is one acute angle of a right triangle whose legs are the contour interval, *CI*, and the horizontal spacing, *H*, between successive contours. The *tangent* of angle α is defined at *CI* divided by *H*. Hence the horizontal distance, *H*, is equal to *CI* times the cotangent of the angle α. From this observation we derive the general statement that the horizontal spacing between isopleths is directly proportional to the cotangent of the gradient measured in degrees.

On a topographic contour map, a hilltop is represented by a contour that forms a continuous loop (*B* in Figure 9.3). A hollow, known as a *topographic depression*, is also delineated by a contour forming a closed loop (*A* in Figure 9.3). A special type of contour line, the *ha-*

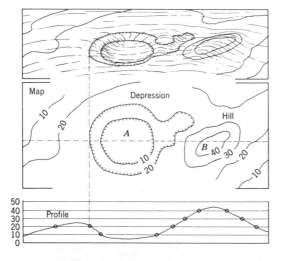

Figure 9.3. Hills and depressions shown by contour lines. (© 1960, John Wiley & Sons, New York.)

chured line, is conventionally used to show a depression.

Construction of a contour topographic map is illustrated in Figure 9.4 by a partially completed map. As a first step, the elevations obtained by surveys are plotted on the map. A line is then drawn to connect those points bearing the same value. Where the plotted values do not coincide with that of the contour, its position is estimated at proportionate distances between points. The same principle is used in preparing any isopleth map. Figure 9.5 shows an isohyetal map partially drawn. (Both maps can be used to practice the drawing of isopleths.)

A *profile*, showing the rise and fall of surface elevations, can be drawn for any line drawn across a contour topographic map, or across any isopleth map. The lower part of Figure 9.3 shows a surface profile constructed along the dashed line of the map above. Horizontal lines on the profile represent contour levels, and these can be scaled as desired.

Once an isopleth map has been drawn, the value at any given point on the surface can be estimated by relative distances from isopleths on either side. In the case of a contour topographic map, surface elevations are estimated as shown in Figure 9.6. Point *B* lies exactly on the 1300-ft contour line and presents no problem of estimation. Point *A*, midway between the 1100-ft and 1200-ft contours, is estimated to lie at 1150 ft. Point *D*, located about one-fifth of the distance from the 1000-ft contour to the 1100-ft contour, is estimated by proportional parts to lie at an elevation of 1020 ft. Summit elevation, point *A*, is difficult to estimate, the value of 1750 ft being a reasonable guess. On many topographic maps elevations are given for all summit points, doing away with the necessity to give an estimate.

B. MAP SCALE

Globes and maps represent the features of the earth's surface on a much smaller size than the actual features. *Scale* is the ratio of length of a given line segment as measured on a globe or a map to the true length of that line on the earth's surface. Scale is given in terms of a *representative fraction (R.F.)*, thus:

$$\frac{1}{100,000}$$

The fraction may also be written as 1:100,000. Any desired units of length may be used with the representative fraction. For example,

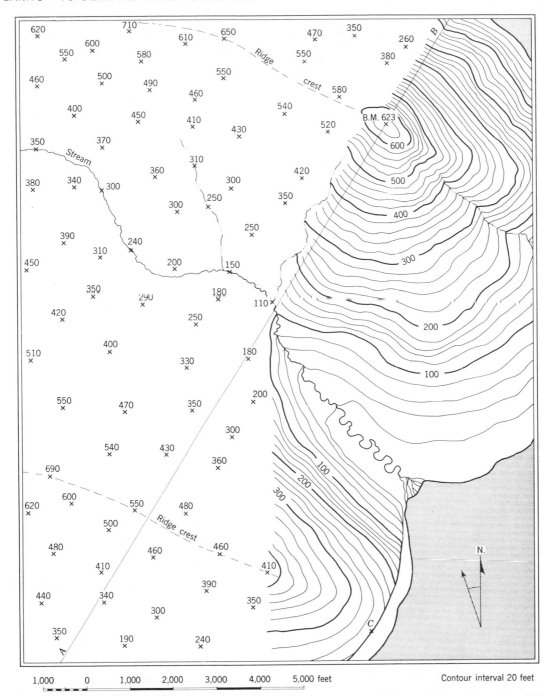

Figure 9.4. Principle of construction of a contour map from elevation data. (© 1960, John Wiley & Sons, New York.)

$$\frac{1}{100,000} = \frac{1 \text{ cm on map}}{100,000 \text{ cm on ground}} = \frac{1 \text{ cm}}{1 \text{ km}}$$

The scale may now be stated as "one centimeter represents one kilometer." Should English units of inches and miles be desired, the denominator is divided by 63,360, which is the number of inches in one mile, thus:

$$\frac{1 \text{ in.}}{100,000 \text{ in.} \div 63,360} = \frac{1 \text{ in.}}{1.57 \text{ mi}}$$

or "one inch represents 1.57 miles." The advantages of the metric system are obvious.

To estimate distances on a map a *graphic scale* is used; it is a line marked off into equal-length units and numbered in distance units. A

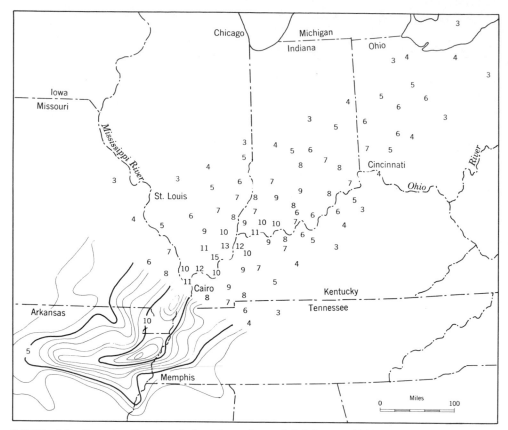

Figure 9.5. Principle of construction of an isohyetal map from rainfall data. (© 1960, John Wiley & Sons, New York.)

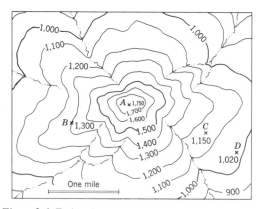

Figure 9.6. Estimating elevations of points on a topographic contour map. (© 1960, John Wiley & Sons, New York.)

graphic scale in English units is illustrated in Figure 9.4. Scales in both English and metric units will be found on all maps of small areas shown in *Planet Earth* except where the maps are purely schematic.

Maps showing a large part of all of the earth's surface will have no graphic or fractional scales attached, for the reason that the scale changes

greatly from one part of the map to another. Only a globe is a true-scale replica of the earth; therefore only a globe can possess a single-scale ratio applicable to the entire surface. World maps have varying scales because the spherical surface of the earth must be distorted by areal expansion or contraction when transformed to a plane surface.

C. GEOLOGIC MAPS AND STRUCTURE SECTIONS

The surface distribution of rock varieties or of rock units differentiated according to age is shown by means of the *areal geologic map* (Figure 9.7). Each rock variety or unit is assigned a distinctive color or pattern. Interest centers upon the lines of contact, which may represent the disconformities between essentially parallel strata or the unconformities between rock bodies of grossly different structures and geologic age. Also represented are contacts between igneous bodies and the surrounding rocks which they have invaded, or the effects of juxtaposition of unlike rock masses by movement on faults. Faults are shown by heavy lines. In general,

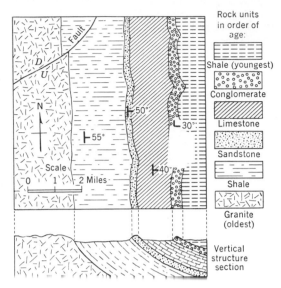

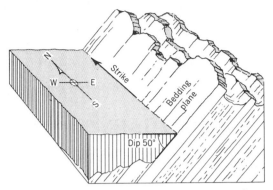

Figure 9.8. Strike and dip illustrated by strata at the shore of a lake. (© 1960, John Wiley & Sons, New York.)

Figure 9.7. A simple geologic map. Below is a structure section drawn along the lower edge of the map area. (© 1960, John Wiley & Sons, New York.)

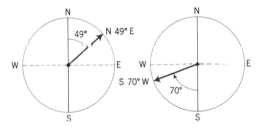

Figure 9.9. Compass-quadrant bearings. (© 1960, John Wiley & Sons, New York.)

contacts and faults are shown by continuous lines where their existence is known with certainty from direct observations on outcrops, and by dotted or broken lines where their presence is suspected or inferred but not confirmed by direct observation.

In mapping and reporting upon geologic relations, it is necessary to describe the attitude of various natural rock planes, including planes of stratification (bedding planes), planes of foliation and cleavage, fault planes, joint planes, planar igneous contacts, and surfaces of unconformity. The *dip* of a natural rock plane is the acute angle formed between the rock plane and an imaginary horizontal plane of reference (Figure 9.8). Dip is stated in degrees and ranges from zero for a horizontal plane to 90° for a vertical plane. Instruments for measurement of dip normally use a level bubble for determination of the horizontal. The direction of dip may also be stated, using compass-quadrant bearings or azimuths.

The *strike* of an inclined rock plane is the direction assumed by the line of intersection between the rock plane and a horizontal plane of reference (Figure 9.8). Geologists convention-

ally state strike in terms of compass-quadrant bearings (Figure 9.9). Any horizontal line has two directions, but it is conventional to give strike with reference to geographic north, for example, N 25° E, or N 67° W. Strike and dip are indicated on a geologic map by T-shaped symbols. The crossbar of the T shows strike, and the other bar shows direction of dip (Figure 9.7).

Distribution of rock bodies at depth is shown by means of the *structure section,* representing the configuration of the rocks as they would appear upon the walls of a straight vertical trench cut to the desired depth (Figure 9.7). The uppermost line of the structure section is a topographic profile upon the ground surface. Considerable vertical exaggeration is commonly used, resulting in the exaggeration of dips from their true values. Structure sections may be drawn by inference based on surface observations or may be based upon rock cores or cuttings brought to the surface by drilling of holes.

BANK 10
SEISMOGRAPHS
AND SEISMIC WAVES

A. SEISMOGRAPHS

In recording an earthquake and analyzing the directions and amounts of the earth motions involved, the mechanical problem is that the instrument itself must be resting on the ground and will therefore also move with the ground. Because the instrument cannot be physically separated from the earth, the seismograph designer must make use of the principle of inertia to overcome the effect of the attachment. *Inertia* is the tendency of any mass to resist a change in a state of rest or of uniform motion in a straight line. The greater the mass of the object, the greater its inertia.

To record an earthquake, then, a very heavy mass, such as an iron ball, might be suspended from a very thin wire or from a flexible coil spring, as shown in Figure 10.1. When the earth moves back and forth or up and down in earthquake wave motion, the large mass will stay almost motionless because the supporting wire or spring flexes easily and does not transmit the motion through to the weight. If a pen is now attached to the mass, so that the point is just touching a sheet of paper wrapped around a moving drum, the pen will produce a wavy line on the paper. Strong shocks will give waves of high *amplitude* (distance from the rest position to a peak or trough), and weak shocks will give waves of low amplitude. When the number of back-and-forth movements per second (i.e., the *frequency*) is higher, the undulations of the line will be more closely crowded.

The seismograph as thus far described is too simple to be actually workable. In the first place the movement of the ground is so very small that the motion must be greatly magnified if it is to produce a record suitable for study. This magnification may be done by a light ray and a

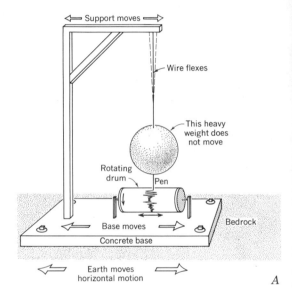

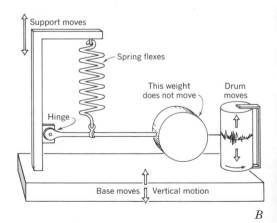

Figure 10.1. Inertia of a large mass provides a means of observing seismic waves. Horizontal motions might be detected by the mechanical arrangement shown in *A*, and vertical motions by that shown in *B*. Neither device would actually be useful unless further refined.

mirror. We know that a small pocket mirror can be used to reflect a spot of sunlight onto the wall of a distant house and that a very slight twist of the hand causes the spot of light to jump many feet. In the seismograph a mirror may be attached to the heavy weight and a very tiny light beam reflected from it onto photographic paper that is attached to the slowly moving drum (Figure 10.2). Of course, either the room is darkened or the instrument is enclosed, so that the pinpoint of light exposes a line on the photographic paper. Later removed and developed, this paper becomes a record of the earthquake known as a *seismogram*.

A second difficulty with the simple apparatus first described is that the earthquake waves rise and fall very slowly, each back-and-forth movement of the ground taking several seconds. The wire from which the heavy weight is suspended would have to be at least 75 ft (23 m) long, otherwise the weight—acting as a simple pendulum—would be set to swinging at about the same frequency as the waves or faster, and no record would be produced. To make a practical seismograph, the weight can be hung from a support hinged like a gate, as shown in Figure 10.2. When the gatepost is tilted slightly, the gate will swing slowly, like a pendulum with a very long wire.

A third difficulty is that any pendulum tends to continue to swing at a natural frequency depending on its length. Because a record of these pendulum movements would tend to obscure the earthquake movements, it is necessary to add a mechanism to *damp* the pendulum, that is, to prevent it from swinging at its own natural frequency.

Modern seismographs make use of magnetic and electronic devices to pick up, amplify, filter, and record the motions of the earth, just as the modern high-fidelity record player uses a magnetic pickup, transistorized amplifier, and

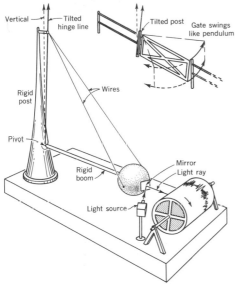

Figure 10.2. Principle of a horizontal, hinge-type pendulum seismograph. Earth motions are greatly magnified by use of a light ray reflected from a mirror.

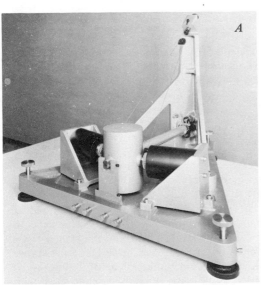

Figure 10.3. (*A*) A horizontal seismograph for detecting long-period seismic waves. Mechanism is basically of the design illustrated in Figure 10.2. (*B*) A vertical seismometer for measuring long-period seismic waves. (Courtesy of the Lamont-Doherty Geological Observatory of Columbia University.)

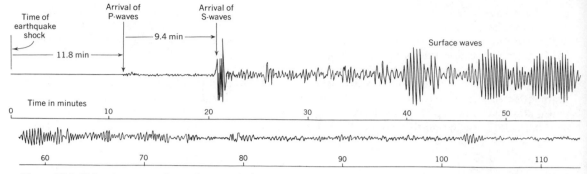

Figure 10.4. This seismogram shows the record of an earthquake whose epicenter was located at a surface distance of 5260 mi (8460 km) from the receiving station, equivalent to 76.4° of arc of the earth's circumference. Figure 10.5 shows the ray paths for this earthquake. [After L. Don Leet (1950), *Earth Waves*, Cambridge, Mass., Harvard Univ. Press.]

magnetic loudspeaker instead of the old-style mechanical pickup head and horn.

To analyze earthquakes adequately, a whole battery of seismographs must be operated simultaneously (Figure 10.3), because each instrument records only the wave motion in one particular line of movement, such as east-west, north-south, or vertically. Then too, earthquake waves include a wide range of frequencies superimposed in a complex way. Just as with a radio receiver, each seismograph is tuned to receive a particular frequency band; therefore several are needed to register the full range.

B. INTERPRETING THE SEISMOGRAM

Figure 10.4 shows a seismogram produced by an earthquake whose epicenter was located at a surface distance of 5260 mi (8460 km) from the observing station. Ray paths for this earthquake are shown in Figure 10.5.

The first indication that a severe earthquake has occurred at a distant point is the sudden beginning of a series of larger-than-average waves called the *primary waves* (P-waves). These waves die down somewhat, then a few minutes later a second burst of activity sets in with the beginning of the *secondary waves* (S-waves). These waves are usually somewhat larger in height than the primary waves. There follow smooth waves that increase greatly in amplitude to a maximum and then slowly die down. These last very high amplitude waves are the *surface waves*. While the primary and secondary waves have traveled through the earth, the surface waves have traveled along the ground surface much as storm swells travel over the sea surface (Figure 10.5).

For an earthquake occurring one-quarter of the globe's circumference away (that is, 90° of arc distant, or 10,000 km), the primary waves

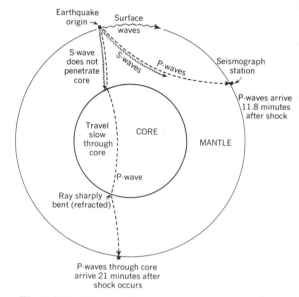

Figure 10.5. Cross section of the earth showing diagrammatically the paths of P-waves, S-waves, and surface waves. [After L. Don Leet (1950), *Earth Waves*, Cambridge, Mass., Harvard Univ. Press.]

will take about 13 min to reach the receiving station, and the secondary waves will begin to arrive about 11 min later.

It was soon apparent to the first students of seismograms that the farther away the earthquake center, or *focus*, the longer the spread of time between the arrival of the primary and secondary wave groups. Both groups start from the focus at the same instant, but the primary group travels faster. Likewise the surface waves travel slowly and come in last. From this discovery, about 1900, came the obvious conclusion that the spread of time between arrival of the wave groups can be used to measure the distance from the focus to the seismograph station.

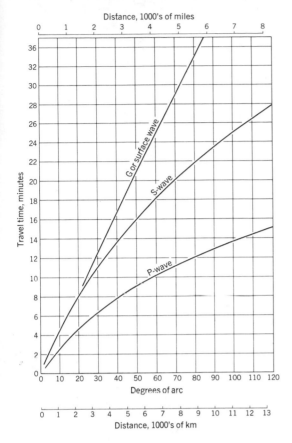

Figure 10.6. Travel-time curves for earthquakes of 100-km (60-mi) depth of focus. [Based on data of C. F. Richter (1958), *Elementary Seismology*, San Francisco, W. H. Freeman and Co., Appendix VIII.]

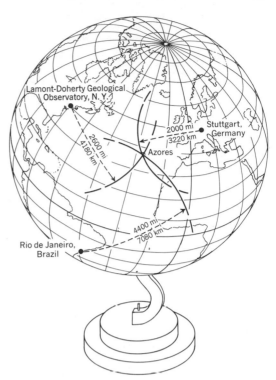

Figure 10.7. Circles drawn from three seismological observatories yield the location of an earthquake epicenter.

Figure 10.6 is a graph on which are plotted *travel-time curves* for primary waves and secondary waves. The difference in times of arrival of the primary and secondary waves, read from the graph as the vertical separation of the two curves, corresponds to distance from focus to seismograph, measured along a great circle on the earth's surface. Units of measure are given in both kilometers and degrees of arc.

In the seismogram shown in Figure 10.4, the difference in arrival times of primary and secondary waves is 9.4 min. As indicated by a dashed line on Figure 10.5, this time difference corresponds to a distance of 5260 mi (8465 km), or an arc of 76.4°.

Using the figure of distance derived from the travel-time curves, a circle of that radius can be drawn on a globe to show the focus of all possible points of origin of the earthquake. When three such circles are drawn from three widely separated observing stations, the earthquake fo-

cus can be located within the limits of a small triangle of error (Figure 10.7).

C. NATURE OF EARTHQUAKE WAVES

When an earthquake shock occurs, several basically different kinds of wave motion are generated. One type, which forms the primary waves, is the same kind of motion as observed in sound waves. As illustrated in Figure 10.8, particles transmitting the primary wave form move only forward and backward in the direction of wave travel. This motion is described as *compression* and *rarefaction* and constitutes a *longitudinal wave*, commonly designated the *P-wave*. We can remember this relation by thinking of the P-wave as a "push" wave. This is easy to keep in mind because the words "primary" and "push" both begin with "P."

In waves of the secondary group, particles transmitting the waves move back and forth at right angles to the direction of wave travel (Figure 10.8). Consequently the secondary wave motion is termed a *transverse wave*, commonly designated the *S-wave*. We may think of these waves as "shake" waves, because like "secondary" the key word begins with "S." In the

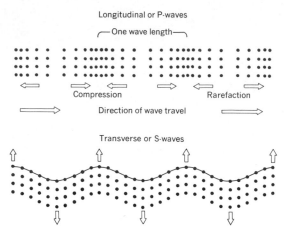

Figure 10.8. Diagrammatic represention of particle motions in longitudinal and transverse seismic waves.

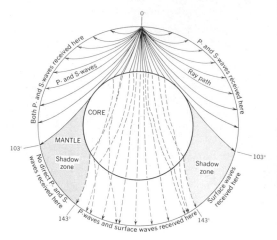

Figure 10.9. Diagrammatic representation of many possible ray paths from a single earthquake source. [After B. Gutenberg (1951), *Internal Constitution of the Earth*, New York, Dover.]

earth, P-waves travel approximately 1.7 times as rapidly as S-waves.

Surface waves are of a still different type and are analogous to waves on water. They were first analyzed mathematically by the English physicist Lord Rayleigh and are therefore known as *Rayleigh waves*. To visualize the motion in Rayleigh waves, refer to Figure 4.27 in *Planet Earth*, which shows particle motion in water waves. One difference is that in Rayleigh waves particles move in retrograde orbits. Surface waves of earthquake origin are, of course, extremely low in height in comparison with common ocean waves, but are similar in that they die out very rapidly with depth below the ground surface. More recently a different type of wave, named the *Love wave* after the physicist who discovered it, has been found to make up a part of the surface wave motion. Love waves have a horizontal motion only, rather than the combination of vertical and horizontal motions of the Rayleigh waves.

D. SEISMIC WAVES AND THE EARTH'S CORE AND MANTLE

Study of earthquake waves has confirmed the existence of the spherical *core* at the earth's center and has added insight into its physical nature. (See Chapter 2 and Figure 2.18 in *Planet Earth* for core dimensions and properties.) If the earth were in a solid state entirely throughout, the P-waves and S-waves would travel through the center in all possible directions, and the various shock waves of any large earthquake could be recorded by a seismograph located directly opposite on the globe.

It was soon found, however, that there is a large region on the side of the globe opposite the earthquake focus where simple S-waves are not received. Evidently they are prevented from passing through a central region, or core, in the earth (Figure 10.9). Physicists know that transverse waves, or S-waves, cannot be sent through a liquid; hence they have agreed that the earth's core is in a liquid state in contrast to the surrounding *mantle*, which is in a solid state. "Solid" in this case may mean either crystalline or glassy, as defined in Chapter 7 of *Planet Earth*. "Solid" also means here that the rock behaves as an elastic solid when subjected to the sudden twists and bends of earthquake waves.

As shown in Figure 10.9, S-waves are received only within a distance of about 103° of arc from the earthquake source. This arc covers somewhat more than one hemisphere. Because of wave bending as the P-waves travel through the core, there is a zone between 103° and 143° distant from the focus where no direct P-waves or S-waves are received, but only surface waves and complex reflected waves. This is the *shadow zone*. A zone beyond 143° receives only P-waves passing through the core, complex reflected waves, and surface waves.

From the extent of the shadow zone the earth's core is calculated to have a radius of 2160 mi (3475 km), a little more than half of the earth's total radius (Figure 2.18 in *Planet Earth*). That the boundary of the core is fairly definite is known because the P-waves are sharply bent at the boundary and their speed drops abruptly to almost half. Figure 2.18 (*Planet*

Earth) shows how the speed of P- and S-waves varies from the surface of the earth to the center.

Using the density information given in Chapter 2 of *Planet Earth,* we may conclude that the outer region of the core is composed of liquid iron of great density, under enormous pressure, and at a high temperature. Confining pressures of 2 to 3 million atmospheres give the liquid metal physical properties unlike anything we can examine at the earth's surface. Although laboratory experiments on the rigidity of rock and speed of earthquake waves have used confining pressures up to 12,000 atmospheres, this pressure is equivalent to a depth of only about 25 mi (40 km).

More recently, evidence from earthquake seismology has revealed that the inner part of the core, to a radius of about 780 mi (1255 km), behaves differently from the rest of the core. This behavior suggests a solid state, rather than the liquid state of the outer core (Figure 2.18, *Planet Earth*).

Another principle of seismology that can be put to use to reveal the nature of the earth's interior is that earthquake waves, both P and S types, travel faster through highly rigid material than through less rigid material. First, however, the meaning of *rigidity* must be made clear. This word applies only to elastic materials—those which bend out of shape when unequal pressures are applied, but which spring back to their original forms when pressures are released. Rigidity is the resistance of an elastic body to a change of shape. Steel and rubber are both elastic, but steel has a much greater rigidity because it bends very much less than rubber under the same deforming stress. (To be strict it should be pointed out that "rigidity" as used here corresponds with the *shear modulus,* a measure of the resistance of an elastic solid to shearing deformation. P-waves are also influenced by the *bulk modulus,* which measures ratio of compressive stress to resulting volume change.)

Rocks in general have a high degree of rigidity, whether composed of crystallized or glassy mineral matter, but among the different rocks there is quite a marked variation. Rigidity can be measured by the physicist in the laboratory, not only under the conditions at the earth's surface, but also under great confining pressures and high temperatures such as those which might be expected many miles deep in the earth.

Because the rigidity of rocks determines the velocity of earthquake waves and because the velocity of these waves at various depths can be

calculated from seismograms, it is possible to make a good guess concerning the kinds of rock in the earth's mantle.

Figure 2.18*D* in *Planet Earth* shows the changes in velocity of P-waves and S-waves with increasing depth in the earth. Notice that the P-wave curve makes an abrupt drop to lower velocity at the mantle-core boundary, and has a secondary inflection at the boundary between liquid outer core and solid inner core. The S-wave curve terminates at the mantle-core boundary. Both curves are upwardly convex in the mantle, showing that the rate of increase in wave velocity diminishes with depth.

Sand, clay, and silt layers, being made up of loose grains, have low rigidity. Of the various kinds of solid rocks, shale, sandstone, and limestone have moderate rigidity (Figure 10.10).

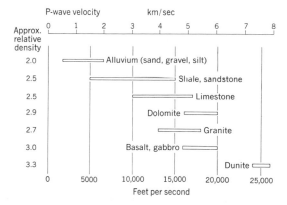

Figure 10.10. Speed of travel of P-waves in various types of rocks.

Next in order of increasing rigidity come granite and the other felsic igneous rocks. Diabase and gabbro, basic rocks which have greater density than granite, have about one-third higher rigidity than granite. Next come the ultramafic rocks, pyroxenite and dunite, with about twice the rigidity of granite and considerably greater density.

The speed of earthquake waves corresponds with this same series: slowest in sand, silt, or clay layers, faster in the sedimentary rocks, higher speed in granite, still faster in basalt and gabbro, and fastest in pyroxenite and dunite. Dolomite, although a sedimentary rock, is exceptional in that it has wave velocities as great as basalt.

In most of the earth's mantle the speed of earthquake waves is so high that only a very rigid and dense rock, such as pyroxenite or dunite, will satisfy the observed conditions. For this reason the mantle is thought to be a zone of solid ultramafic (ultrabasic) rock made up of magnesium iron silicate minerals. The mantle is about 1790 mi (2880 km) thick (Figure 2.18 in *Planet Earth*).

E. SEISMIC WAVES AND CRUSTAL STRUCTURE

The earth's *crust* is a layer varying from 5 to 25 mi (3 to 40 km) in thickness. It averages 10 mi (17 km) in thickness when calculated as uniformly spread over the globe. The crust is distinguished from the mantle by the presence of a rather abrupt and clearly defined change in the velocity of seismic waves, indicating that there is a corresponding abrupt change in rigidity of the rock from crust to mantle. A change in rigidity indicates in turn an abrupt change in mineral composition or in physical state of the rocks.

Seismology has provided the means to interpret the thickness and structure of the earth's crust. Where an earthquake has a focus close to the surface and is located only a few hundred miles away from the seismograph station, the seismic waves do not penetrate the earth more than about 100 mi (160 km) before they are gradually turned back toward the surface and reach the seismograph. Interpretation of the complex wave records will reveal the velocities at which the waves traveled at different depths.

Natural earthquakes are unfortunately unpredictable in time and place of occurrence except in a very general way; therefore, the best source of information about the shallow zones of the earth comes from man-made shocks. One method is to make use of blasts set off at rock quarries and to record them with portable seismographs at various distances from the blasts. In analyzing shallow zones for possible petroleum-bearing structures, small dynamite explosions are used.

Generally speaking, rigidity of crust and mantle rocks increases with depth. Very simply, two possibilities may be considered for the subsurface structure. Figure 10.11, top, shows the case of gradual increase in rock rigidity with depth. As the shock wave penetrates this rock, it encounters regions of progressively faster travel. This change results in a continuous bending, or *refraction,* of the wave path, or ray, in such a way as to turn it toward a path parallel with the surface. Continued bending of the path causes the wave to return eventually to the surface, following a curved path. Continuous refraction of this type might indicate that not only does the rock become more rigid because of increasing confining pressure at depth, but that it also is changing gradually in composition to a rock consisting of

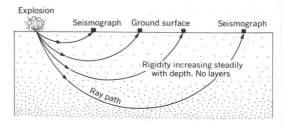

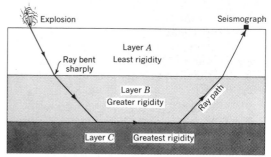

Figure 10.11. Bending of seismic waves as they travel through rock layers of differing degrees of rigidity.

denser minerals—that is, from granite (felsic) to basalt (mafic) and then to ultramafic rock without any abrupt change.

Figure 10.11, bottom, shows the case in which there exist layers of rock, each of uniform rigidity within itself, but with each successively deeper layer changing abruptly to higher rigidity. In this case a particular ray of the shock wave travels in a straight line through each layer but is refracted sharply as it enters the next layer. When it strikes a new layer at a certain critical angle, the wave travels along the contact between layers for a certain distance and is then turned upward to return to the surface. When the seismograms of several recording stations are compared, the subsurface paths of the seismic waves can be reconstructed and the velocities of wave travel estimated for different depths. This information in turn makes possible the selection of rock varieties whose physical properties fit the observed wave velocities.

Waves of both shallow earthquakes and surface explosions show quite definitely that the continents consist of a platelike crust, averaging about 20 mi (33 km) thick, resting upon quite different rock of the mantle. As shown in Figure 7.8 in *Planet Earth,* the continental crust consists of largely granitic rock in the upper part and of largely basaltic rock in the lower part.

It is known that the P-waves near the surface travel at about 3.8 mi (6.2 km) per second, which is expected in granite rock, and that this velocity increases gradually or abruptly to the base of the crust, where it is about 4.3 mi (7 km) per second, a velocity expected in basaltic rock at this depth. At about 20 mi (33 km) depth, on the average, the velocity increases abruptly to more than 5 mi (8 km) per second, a speed to be expected of an ultramafic rock, such as peridotite. S-waves undergo a corresponding velocity increase with depth. This surface of sudden increase in wave velocity, which separates the crust above from the mantle below, is named the *Mohorovičić discontinuity* after the Yugoslav seismologist who first recognized the discontinuity in 1909 from the records of shallow-focus earthquakes.

For obvious reasons, it has become accepted practice to designate this discontinuity as the *Moho*, or simply as the *M-discontinuity*.

At the margins of the continent the crust thins rapidly, and at the same time its base becomes much shallower. Here the M-discontinuity is found at a depth of about 7.5 mi (12 km) below sea level (Figure 7.8 in *Planet Earth*). The basaltic rock of the lower part of the continental plate extends out over the ocean-basin floors as a crustal layer 3 to 5 mi (5 to 8 km) thick. P-wave velocities in the lower basaltic crust range from 4.0 to 4.4 mi (6.5 to 7.1 km) per second.

BANK 13
BIOSTRATIGRAPHY AND EVOLUTION

A. BIOSTRATIGRAPHIC UNITS

We have seen in Chapter 13 in *Planet Earth* that a fauna, which is a distinctive assemblage of fossil species, is useful in correlating strata from place to place. It is therefore desirable in some instances to define a unit of strata in terms of the fossils alone, and without regard to the lithologic characteristics of those strata. So defined, the strata comprise a *biostratigraphic unit.* A biostratigraphic unit distinguished by a particular fossil species or a particular fossil fauna is referred to as a *zone.*

The Cambrian Bright Angel formation of Grand Canyon provides a fine example of a *faunal zone.* It can be seen on the Bright Angel Trail about one-quarter of a mile north of Indian Gardens in Bright Angel Canyon. This distinctive faunal zone is so narrow in vertical extent that it is essentially restricted to a single *horizon.* Two distinctive fossils in this horizon are trilobite species named *Glossopleura mckeei* and *Alokistocare althea* (Figure 13.1*A* and *B*)—the first name refers to the genus, the second name to the species. In addition, the fauna consists of a third trilobite, *Anoria tontoensis,* a cystid (similar to a "sea lily") named *Eocrinus multibrachiatus,* a conical-shelled gastropod (snail), *Hyolithes* sp. ("sp." means "no specific name assigned"), and a brachiopod, *Lingulella mckeei.* The last three fossils are illustrated in Figure 13.1*C, D,* and *E.* The names and photographs of these fossils are given here to provide a real example of the working procedures of the stratigrapher. The *Glossopleura-Alokistocare* faunal zone can be traced in exposures of the Bright Angel formation for a horizontal distance of almost 180 mi (290 km) across northern Arizona. Wherever this zone is located it will be found to contain the same species. The same fauna is not, however, duplicated above or below this zone.

The thin faunal zone we have examined in detail is interpreted as having been deposited at very nearly the same time throughout its 180-mi extent. If this interpretation is valid, the horizon serves to synchronize the sequence of deposition over a large area. One might describe this horizon as a "time line" or, in formal terms, an *isochron* (*iso,* same, plus *chron,* time). In three dimensions, the faunal horizon would define a "time plane," or an *isochronous surface.*

B. STRATIGRAPHIC COLUMNS AND THEIR CORRELATION

The stratigrapher conducts his investigation by moving about from place to place, examining the column of strata of a given age group wherever it is well exposed. Each lithologic unit is carefully measured and described. Fossils, if present, are collected and identified. Samples of rock may be taken for laboratory study, including microscopic examination and chemical analysis. Data are plotted to scale in a narrow vertical column, known as a *stratigraphic column.* A number of such columns obtained on a line of cross-country traverse are placed side by side, spaced to horizontal scale. Connecting lines are drawn to correlate lithologic units (formations and members) and faunal zones.

Figure 13.2 is an assemblage of stratigraphic columns for the Cambrian of northern Arizona from the Grand Wash Cliffs on the west to the Little Colorado River on the east. Localities follow the winding course of Grand Canyon, since the Cambrian is not exposed elsewhere. Lithologic units are shown by conventional patterns, explained in the accompanying key. Dashed

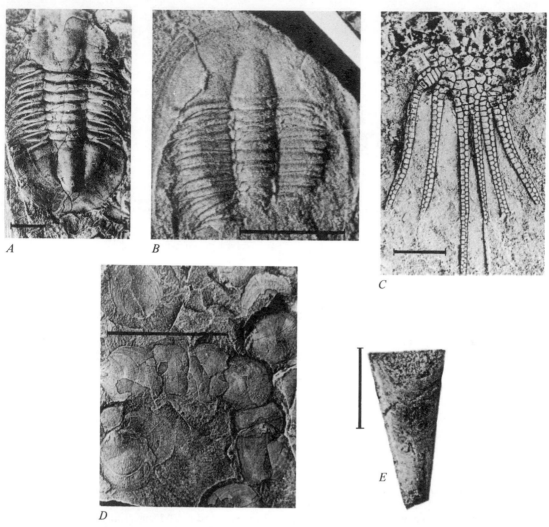

Figure 13.1. Representative specimens of fossils of the *Glossopleura-Alokistocare* fauna of the Cambrian strata of Grand Canyon. Length of bar is 1 cm (0.4 in.). (*A*) *Glossopleura mckeei,* a trilobite. (*B*) *Alokistocare althea,* a trilobite. (*C*) *Eocrinus multibrachiatus,* a crinoid. (*D*) *Lingulella mckeei,* a brachiopod. (*E*) *Hyolithes* sp., a gastropod. [Photographs from C. E. Resser (1945), Washington, D.C., Carnegie Inst. of Washington, Publication 563, Part II, Plates 16, 18, 19, 21, and 22.]

lines connect corresponding lithologic contacts. Because present-day elevation of the land has no particular significance so far as Cambrian time is concerned, an arbitrary horizon line has been established at a point in the middle of the Muav formation. The sections are then scaled up and down from this arbitrary zero reference line. It would be equally feasible to use the top of the Muav formation as the zero reference line, except that an erosional disconformity exists there and we do not know what thicknesses of Cambrian strata were formerly present above that surface.

In interpreting the stratigraphic sections of Figure 13.2, we notice several points of interest. First, the total thickness of the Cambrian increases toward the west. Thickening westward is brought about in a rather complex manner. We do not find that each lithologic unit found at Grand Canyon merely thickens proportionately toward the west while maintaining its lithologic identity. To give one exception, new lithologic units appear in the section, and these tend to thicken westward. An example is the Rampart Cave member. In the Bass Trail section this member is represented by only a thin dolomite

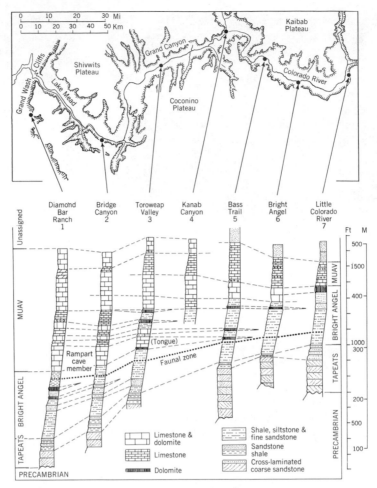

Figure 13.2. Columnar stratigraphic sections and index map of Cambrian formations of the Grand Canyon. [Modified and simplified from E. D. McKee (1945), *Cambrian History of the Grand Canyon Region,* Washington, D.C., Carnegie Inst. of Washington, Publication 563, Part I, p. 18, Figure 2A, and p. 19, Figure 2B.]

bed in the middle of the Bright Angel shale. It is absent in the Bright Angel section, about 10 mi (16 km) to the east. Toward the west this dolomite bed thickens and changes in composition from a rusty-brown dolomite to a mottled limestone with dolomite beds. Along the Grand Wash Cliffs still farther west the Rampart Cave member is a massive unit about 180 ft (85 m) thick. This unit is described as a *tongue.* It is interpreted to mean that accumulation of carbonate sediment was abundant in the western part of the region, diminished progressively eastward, and ceased at a point near what is now the eastern part of Grand Canyon. It is also obvious that shale strata assigned to the upper half of the Bright Angel formation in the eastern part of the traverse are correlated in time with carbonate strata assigned to the Muav formation in the

western end of the traverse. Evidently the formations defined on the basis of lithology are not everywhere of the same age. Notice that the line representing the *Glossopleura-Alokistocare* faunal zone starts at the west near the top of the Bright Angel formation, but ends up at the east near the bottom of that formation.

C. TIME UNITS AND LITHOFACIES

Let us pursue the Cambrian stratigraphy of Northern Arizona by a change of approach. The measured sections of Cambrian strata shown in Figure 13.2 can be reconstituted into a schematic diagram in which horizontal lines represent planes of equal time or isochronous surfaces (Figure 13.3). Actual thickness of units is disregarded in this representation. Cover the diagram with a sheet of paper. Now move the paper grad-

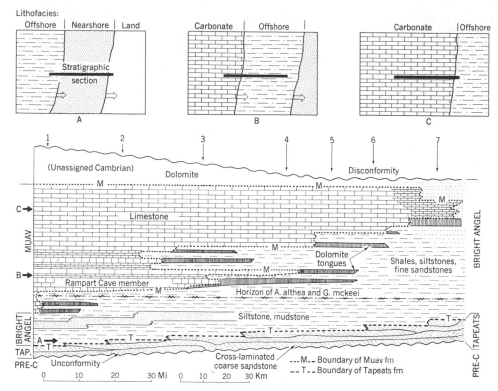

Figure 13.3. Lithofacies-time diagram of the same Cambrian stratigraphic sequence shown in Figure 13.2. Numbers refer to locations of stratigraphic sections shown in Figure 13.2. Horizontal lines represent isochrones. Schematic lithofacies maps above apply to time lines marked *A, B,* and *C* on lower diagram. [Lower diagram modified from E. D. McKee (1945), *Cambrian History of the Grand Canyon Region,* Washington, D.C., Carnegie Inst. of Washington, Publication 563, Part I, p. 14, Figure 1.]

ually up, keeping the edge horizontal and uncovering the diagram from the bottom upward. As this is done, the sequence of deposition emerges to view. Lines of dots on the diagram represent the formation boundaries.

Starting with the base of the Tapeats sandstone, notice that deposition begins in the west and spreads eastward up the undulating slope of the erosional surface on the Precambrian rocks beneath. Here we see *transgression* of strata, caused by a rising sea level encroaching upon a landmass (or sinking landmass gradually becoming submerged beneath an ocean of fixed sea level). At certain points during the transgression the formation boundary makes an abrupt reverse inflection, showing a temporary reversal of the transgression. The reverse trend is known as *regression.* Notice, also, that as deposition of Tapeats sandstone progresses eastward it is accompanied in the west by deposition of shale of the lower Bright Angel formation.

Progressing further up the diagram, carbonate deposition begins first at the west end of the sec-

tion, transgressing eastward for a time, then regressing to the west to leave a tongue of limestone and dolomite. Several such tongues are recorded. Tongues of shale extend westward between the dolomite tongues. The gross pattern is known as *intertonguing.* Finally, however, the transgression brought a continuous environment of carbonate deposition to this region and the remainder of the accumulation is solidly limestone and dolomite.

In summary, the Grand Canyon region in the first part of the Cambrian period was a landmass exposed to erosion. Gradually the landmass subsided, beginning first in the west. The sea invaded from the west, gradually submerging the land. Starting in early Cambrian time the shoreline thus crossed the region from west to east and by late middle Cambrian time lay somewhere far to the east of this region. As the shoreline encroached upon the land, sand deposition accompanied it, followed to seaward by clay and silt deposition, and still farther out by carbonate sediment deposition. Evidently three depositional environments are represented in the time sequence at any given geographical location. We can assume that the environment was controlled by water depth and by distance from land.

The stratigrapher has developed a method of expressing the general appearance, composition, and depositional environment of a rock unit by means of a single designation, known as *facies*. As defined in a dictionary, the word "facies" means "general appearance" (it comes from the Latin word for "face"). To the stratigrapher, facies takes on a more specialized meaning and must be narrowed down to one of a number of reference frames. For example, facies relating to the gross physical qualities of rocks within a unit is known as *lithofacies*. In the case of the Cambrian strata of Grand Canyon, there are at least three distinct lithofacies: (1) a near-shore sand facies of the Tapeats formation, (2) an offshore silt-clay facies represented by the Bright Angel shales, and (3) a carbonate facies represented by the Muav formation and its tongues. *Biofacies* is a general description of the faunal assemblage within strata and can be independent of lithology.

Above the time-section in Figure 13.3 are three maps showing three stages in the Cambrian sedimentation. The three principal facies are shown by line patterns. Reconstructions of this kind are known as *paleogeographic maps*. They supplement the stratigraphic cross sections by giving area relationships, including shorelines, lands, shallow seas, and troughs.

D. EVOLUTIONARY CHARTS OF PLANTS AND ANIMALS

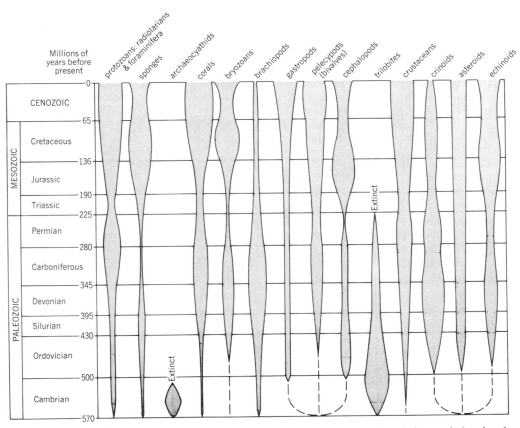

Figure 13.4. Evolution of the major groups of invertebrate marine animals. Width of band shows relative abundance of groups. [Data from A. L. McAlester (1968), *The History of Life*, Englewood Cliffs, N.J., Prentice-Hall, pp. 60-61, Figure 3-7.]

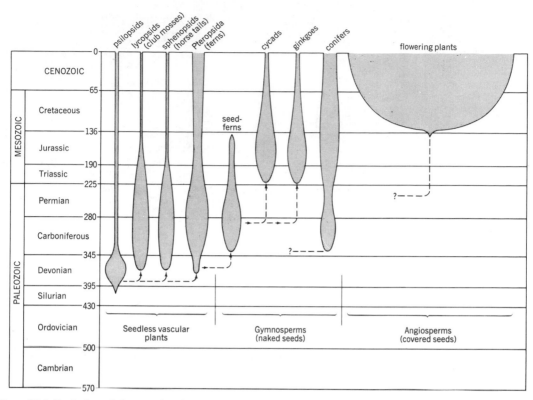

Figure 13.5. Evolution of the vascular plants. Width of band shows relative abundance of groups. [Data from A. L. McAlester (1968), *The History of Life,* Englewood Cliffs, N.J., Prentice-Hall, pp. 86-87, Figure 5-2.]

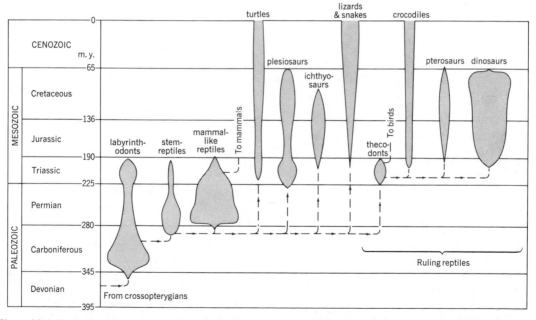

Figure 13.6. Evolution of the reptiles. Width of band shows relative abundance of groups. [Data from A. L. McAlester (1968), *The History of Life,* Englewood Cliffs, N.J., Prentice-Hall, pp. 104-105, Figure 6-1.]

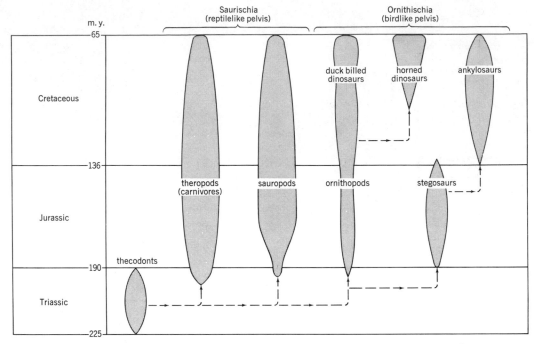

Figure 13.7. Evolution of the dinosaurs. Width of band shows relative abundance of groups. [Data from A. L. McAlester (1968), *The History of Life,* Englewood Cliffs, N.J., Prentice-Hall, p. 112, Figure 6-9.]

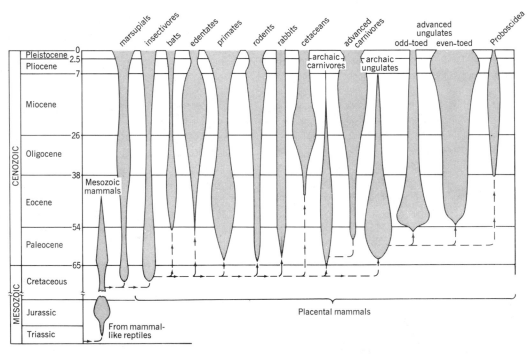

Figure 13.8. Evolution of the mammals. Width of band shows relative abundance of groups. [Data from A. L. McAlester (1968), *The History of Life,* Englewood Cliffs, N.J., Prentice-Hall, pp. 122-123, Figure 6-19.]

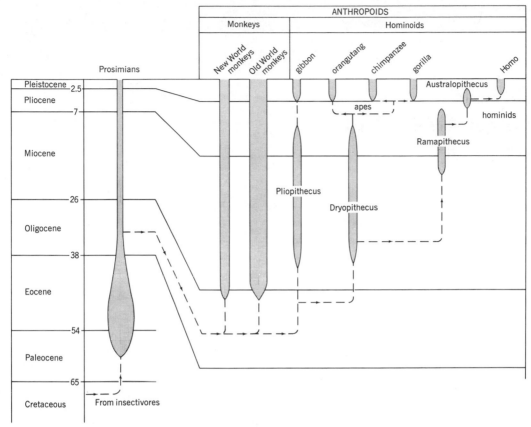

Figure 13.9. Evolution of the primates. [Data from A. L. McAlester (1968), *The History of Life,* Englewood Cliffs, N.J., Prentice-Hall, pp. 130-131, Figure 7-1.]

BANK 14

NORTH AMERICA IN
THE CENOZOIC ERA

A. EVOLUTION OF THE APPALACHIAN LANDSCAPE

The present configuration of the Appalachian highlands, that mountainous belt extending from Georgia to Maine and beyond into the Maritime Provinces of Canada, has its origins in a sequence of events beginning in the Paleozoic Era and continuing through the Mesozoic and Cenozoic Eras. The geological evolution of the Appalachians is illustrated by a series of block diagrams showing development of the Hudson Valley region in New York State (Figure 14.1).

Block A The accumulation of sediments during the Paleozoic Era is shown. Sedimentation was interrupted by orogenies at least twice, but persisted generally into the Permian Period, when the Appalachian Orogeny deformed the Paleozoic strata, along with all older rocks beneath them, for the final time.

Block B The Paleozoic strata were folded and thrust-faulted into a mountain range at the close of Permian time. Denudation of this range occurred through the Triassic Period.

Block C By the close of Triassic time a peneplain existed over the entire region. Denudation had exposed the mountain roots, revealing metamorphic rocks of lowermost Paleozoic age and late Precambrian age on the east. Toward the west folded strata of lower Paleozoic age were beveled.

Block D Late in the Triassic Period the crust was broken into great fault blocks. Evidently, the lithospheric plate beneath was being subjected to extension, such as that found active today in the Basin-and-Range region of the western United States. Erosion of the tilted fault blocks produced sediment (red beds) which partially filled the basins produced by down-faulting. Basaltic lavas were also extruded over these sediments. This was the last major dia-strophic movement to affect the Appalachian region.

Block E In Jurassic and early Cretaceous time denudation again reduced the region to a peneplain, exposing still more deeply the mountain roots.

Block F Epeirogenic crustal rise (actually a succession of uplifts) allowed denudation to be renewed. Weak rock belts were quickly reduced by erosion, leaving the harder rock formations to stand boldly in relief, as we find the region today. The Cenozoic Era is thus represented by denudation, renewed repeatedly by episodes of broad crustal rise, perhaps representing isostatic uplifts required by erosional removal of the rock mass.

B. NORTH AMERICA IN CRETACEOUS TIME

The upper part of the Cretaceous Period in North America provides a representative example of geosynclinal development and paleographic interpretation. Figure 14.2 is a paleogeographic map of the upper Cretaceous showing the extent of existing strata drawn upon a map of the modern continent. The most striking feature is the great Rocky Mountain Seaway extending from Alberta to Mexico. In this seaway lay the Rocky Mountain Geosyncline, shown in cross section in Figure 14.3. Great thicknesses of detrital sediments were brought into the geosyncline from Cordilleran highlands to the west. These mountains had been produced by folding and thrusting in the Nevadian orogeny which closed the Jurassic Period in this part of the continent. Farther to the west, along what is now the Pacific coast, lay another belt of marine deposition consisting of a series of deep basins. Sediments deposited in these basins were derived both from the Cordilleran highlands and

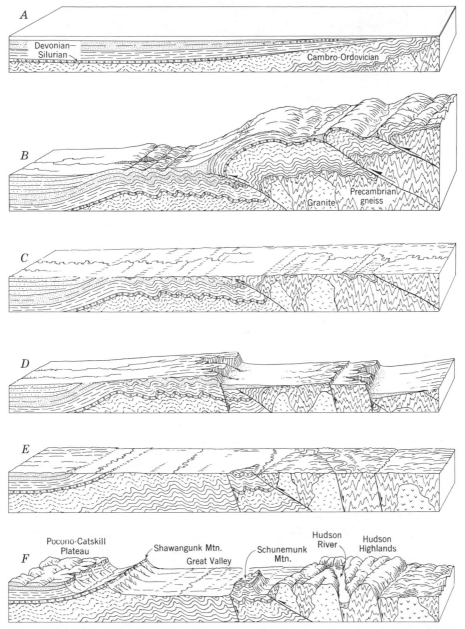

Figure 14.1. This series of block diagrams shows the geologic development of the Hudson Valley region in New York State. The long dimension of the block runs northwest-southeast, across the grain of the geologic structure. (*A*) Strata accumulated in a shallow Devonian seaway. (*B*) Folding and thrusting occurred during the Appalachian revolution at the close of the Paleozoic Era. (*C*) Folds were largely beveled and mountain roots exposed in the development of a peneplain in the Triassic Period. (*D*) Block faulting at the close of the Triassic Period raised tabular mountain masses separated by steep escarpments. (*E*) By the middle of the Cenozoic Era a much later peneplanation had reduced the region to an undulating plain. (*F*) The modern landscape owes its relief features to different degrees of resistance of the rock bodies to erosion.

from volcanic islands that are postulated to have lain to the west.

While the western part of the continent was experiencing a crustal evolution of geosynclinal deposition and orogeny, the eastern half was a stable continental platform, as it had been throughout Jurassic time as well. Denudation of the exposed Canadian shield and its southern extension into the United States, continuing through both Jurassic and Cretaceous Periods,

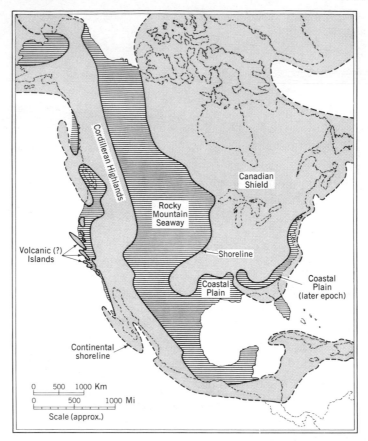

Figure 14.2. Paleogeographic map of North America in upper Cretaceous time, specifically, the *Turonian Epoch*. Extensive parts of the map are conjectural. The dark pattern shows areas receiving marine sedimentary deposits. The light pattern shows hypothetical continental limits. [Redrawn and simplified from a map by Charles Schuchert (1955), *Atlas of Paleogeographical Maps of North America*, New York, John Wiley & Sons, Map No. 73.]

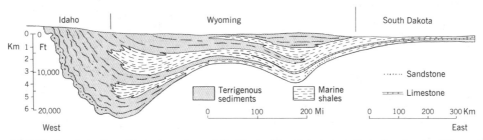

Figure 14.3. Restored stratigraphic cross section of the Rocky Mountain geosyncline, showing conditions at the close of the Cretaceous Period. Tongues of terrestrial sediments derived from sources to the west interfinger with tongues of marine sediments dominant on the east. [Redrawn and simplified from M. Kay and E. H. Colbert (1965), *Stratigraphy and Life History*, New York, John Wiley & Sons, p. 442, Figure 18-25.]

had reduced this region to a peneplain. But in lower Cretaceous time the continental margins began to subside and to become submerged by shallow seas of a widening continental shelf. Submergence began in the Gulf Coast area and Florida, then spread along the eastern seaboard states until an inner limit was reached, as shown in Figure 14.2. These Cretaceous strata, with the Cenozoic strata which now rest upon them, today comprise the *Coastal Plain* geologic province of the United States. We can say, then, that the architecture of the eastern half of the North American continent was largely completed by the close of the Cretaceous Period.

Late in Cretaceous time, the thick geosynclinal sediments of the Rocky Mountain geosyncline, shown in Figure 14.3, began to be raised into a chain of great anticlinal ranges. Today, these up-arched structures constitute the Rocky Mountains. This orogenic development, along with other Cretaceous orogenic movements in the western United States, is usually designated the *Laramian orogeny*. As in the case of the Appalachian orogeny that closed the Paleozoic Era, the Laramian orogeny was not a single terminal event, but was spread over a large part of the Cretaceous Period. Accompanying orogeny was intrusion of a number of great batholiths of the western United States. These are outlined in Figure 7.12 in *Planet Earth*.

C. RADIOCARBON AGE DETERMINATION

Assignment of ages in years-before-present to deposits and events of the Holocene Epoch and the last cycle of glaciation and interglaciation of the Pleistocene Epoch has been made possible by the *carbon-14*, or *radiocarbon*, method of age determination. In the earth's upper atmosphere, at levels above 10 mi (16 km), atoms of ordinary nitrogen (nitrogen-14) are subject to bombardment by neutrons created by highly energetic cosmic particles (cosmic rays) penetrating the atmosphere from outer space (see Chapter 15 and Figure 15.21 in *Planet Earth*). Upon being struck, an atom of nitrogen-14 absorbs the impacting neutron and emits a proton. The nitrogen atom is thus transformed into an isotope of carbon, carbon-14, which quickly combines with oxygen to form carbon dioxide.

Carbon-14 is radioactive and decays back to nitrogen-14. The half-life of carbon-14 is 5730 ± 40 years. (Refer to Chapter 7 in *Planet Earth* for explanation of radioactive decay and half-life, and to Chapter 10 for methods of radiometric age determination.)

The rate of production of carbon-14 in the upper atmosphere is assumed to be constant. Therefore atmospheric carbon dioxide that is taken up by plants and animals will contain a fixed proportion of carbon-14 relative to the total amount of ordinary carbon (carbon-12). From an initial point in time marked by the death of the organism, the proportion of carbon-14 in the organic structure declines steadily, following the exponential curve of decline. By precision measurements of the extremely small amounts of carbon-14 in a sample of organic matter, the age in years of that matter can be estimated to within a fairly small percentage of error. While the very short half-life of carbon-14 makes it an excellent tool for age determinations in the last few tens of thousands of years, the uncertainty of measurement increases at such a rate that the present limit of usefulness is about $-40,000$ years.

The radiocarbon method of age determination was developed in about 1950 by Willard F. Libby of the Institute for Nuclear Studies of the University of Chicago. Age determinations were made of such materials as charcoal, shells, wood, and peat derived from archaeological sites and glacial deposits. Materials whose age was documented from other historical records served as a check upon the accuracy of the method. By 1952 Libby's laboratory had made age determinations of a large number of carefully selected samples. Other laboratories were soon set up and the radiocarbon method has since been established as one of the most important research tools in geological and archaeological research.

A highly significant event was the dating of wood from trees overwhelmed by the last known ice advance at Two Creeks, Wisconsin (see Figure 14.5). This date, $11,850 \pm 100$ years before present, proved to be about half the age previously estimated.

In recent years discrepancies have been found in radiocarbon dates as checked against dates determined by such independent means as tree-ring counts and recorded human history. There are reasons to suspect that the rate of production of carbon-14 has not, in fact, been constant in the past. There is no reason to doubt the constancy of interception of cosmic particles by the earth. However, the effectiveness of these particles in penetrating the outer atmosphere, and hence in producing carbon-14, is influenced by the strength of the earth's external magnetic field (Chapter 2 in *Planet Earth*). Greater strength of the magnetic field tends to reduce cosmic particle penetration, while a weaker field permits particles to penetrate more readily. The exclusion of cosmic particles during periods of magnetic "bays" in magnetic storms is well documented. We have seen that disturbances of the external magnetic field are caused by solar flares, and that the frequency of these flares varies in the same 11-year cycle as does the frequency of sunspots. It is likely, therefore, that the rate of production of carbon-14 follows this and perhaps other cycles of solar activity. In view of observed discrepancies in radiocarbon dates, it is recommended that a given age determination be considered to have a probable absolute error of at least 5%.

D. WISCONSINAN STAGE IN THE MIDDLE WEST

Sediments produced during the Wisconsinan Glaciation are said to comprise the *Wisconsinan Stage*. The term "stage" is regarded as a time-stratigraphic unit, since it is defined according to the sedimentary record deposited within specified time limits. Within the Wisconsinan Stage are *substages* consisting of stratigraphic units produced during a number of episodes of glacial advance and recession within any given region. These substages receive names of largely local significance. Within the duration of a given substage the ice front may have advanced one or more times, leaving a till deposit and a terminal moraine. Between ice advances soils were developing on exposed tills, low areas were receiving deposits of glaciolacustrine silts, and bogs were accumulating peat. Forests may have grown on the exposed surfaces, to be overridden

by ice of the next advance. In the bordering region south of the glacial limit layers of loess were deposited on uplands, while alluvium was spread over the valley floors.

In the states of Wisconsin and Illinois five substages are recognized within the Wisconsinan Stage. We have selected this region to illustrate the identification of substages because it is centrally located in the continent and is unusually rich in details of Pleistocene stratigraphy. Figure 14.4 is a diagram showing these substages. The vertical axis of the diagram is scaled in time, and the horizontal axis in latitude, north being toward the right. Advance and recession of the ice front is represented by tongues of till deposition entering from the north, reaching a southern limit, then receding north beyond the limits of the diagram. The position and nature of the deposits between tills and in advance of the ice is suggested by various patterns.

Substages in Illinois and Wisconsin are named, from oldest to youngest, *Altonian, Farmdalian, Woodfordian, Twocreekan,* and *Valderan*. These

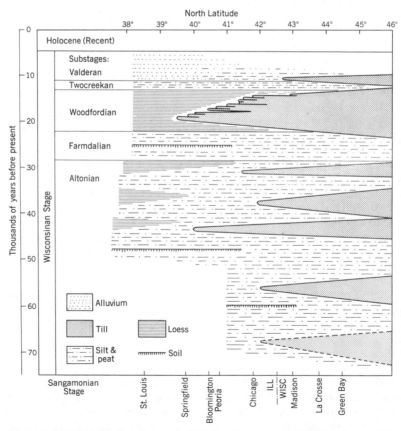

Figure 14.4. Time-latitude diagram showing sequence of Wisconsinan deposits in Wisconsin and Illinois. Diagram is largely schematic and cannot be interpreted in terms of thicknesses of deposits. [After J. C. Frye, H. B. Willman, and R. F. Black (1965), in *The Quaternary of the United States,* H. E. Wright, Jr., and D. G. Frey, Eds., Princeton N.J., Princeton Univ. Press, p. 51, Figure 5.]

substages comprise the *Wisconsinan Stage*. The Altonian Substage began at about − 75,000 years. However, no radiocarbon dates are available to determine the onset of the Altonian Substage. Silt, peat, tills, and loess of Altonian age rest directly upon soil of the Sangamonian Stage. Four and possibly five ice advances occurred in the Altonian Substage. The Farmdalian Substage is a comparatively short interval of major glacial withdrawal, falling between −28,000 and −23,000 years, during which silt and peat were deposited. There followed the Woodfordian Substage, in which a major ice advance occurred, reaching to the maximum limit of any advance within the Wisconsinan Stage. Ice recession, punctuated by many minor readvances, took place in an interval of about 8000 years, leaving more than 30 recessional moraines in Illinois. A short episode of glacier recession, the Twocreekan Substage, saw the deposition of more peat and silt and the growth of forests of spruce, birch, and jackpine (Figure 14.5). Evidences of Man and remains of various mammals are found in this time interval. In the Valderan Substage ice advanced for the last time, overriding the forests and soils of the previous substage. Final ice recession is judged to have occurred at about −10,000 years, which is generally taken as the point in time ending the Pleistocene Epoch and beginning the Holocene Epoch. However, some specialists in the glacial and related deposits of this area extend the Valderan Substage to −5000 years to include alluvial deposits formed following ice recession.

The above chronology of substages of the Wisconsinan Stage is cited as an example of the actual complexity of the record. If one were to look at similar sequences for other parts of North America, he would find a somewhat different set of substages and names for each locality. We should expect to find a reasonable agreement on the existence of substages such as the Farmdalian and Twocreekan on the grounds that a major

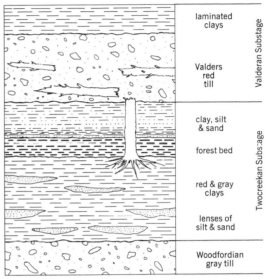

Figure 14.5. The Two Creeks forest bed, exposed near Manitowoc, Wisconsin, was developed in a substage of mild climate, but was subsequently overridden by ice advance in the Valderan Substage. [After J. L. Hough (1958), *Geology of the Great Lakes,* Urbana, Univ. of Illinois Press, p. 102, Figure 31.]

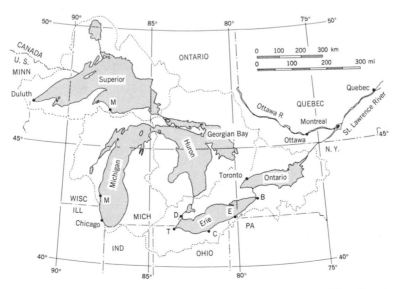

Figure 14.6. General map of the Great Lakes region. Drainage areas outlined in dotted line. (Based on U.S. Lake Survey charts.)

recession of the continental ice sheet must have affected all areas of equivalent latitude at about the same time. We should also expect the major ice advances to be reflected in all records, although ice lobes may have advanced at different rates and to different limits from one region to another.

E. HISTORY OF THE GREAT LAKES

The five Great Lakes (Figure 14.6) rank as follows in terms of surface area:

	sq mi	sq km
Superior (2)	31,800	82,400
Huron	23,000	59,600
Michigan (6)	22,400	58,000
Erie (12)	9,900	26,000
Ontario (14)	7,500	19,400

Numbers in parentheses give ranking among all

world lakes in surface area. Lake Superior is second only to the Caspian Sea, which is over five times larger. Elevations and depths of the Great Lakes are shown by a profile in Figure 14.7. Superior has the greatest depth, 1330 ft (405 m); Michigan, Huron, and Ontario are of moderate depths, 800 to 900 ft (240 to 275 m); while by comparison Erie is very shallow, 200 ft (60 m).

A complicating factor in the history of the Great Lakes has been a downwarping of the earth's crust under the load of glacial ice and a subsequent upwarping following removal of ice load. Figure 14.8 is a schematic diagram to illustrate the principle as it applies to the Great Lakes region. In *Phase 1* the crust is shown to be warped down beneath the ice sheet while a proglacial lake lies to the south of the ice front.

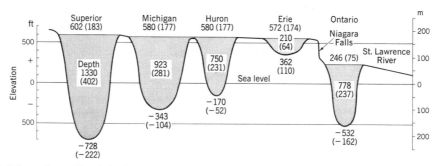

Figure 14.7. Schematic profile of the Great Lakes. Surface elevations given above and greatest depths at bottom. Figures in feet, with meters in parentheses. (Data from Corps of Engineers, U.S. Army.)

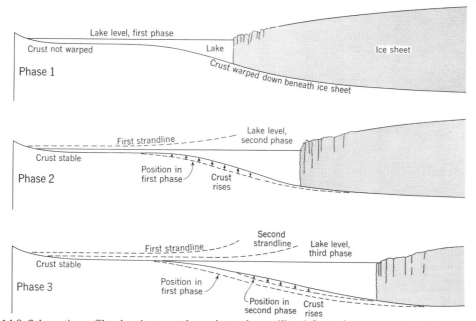

Figure 14.8. Schematic profiles showing crustal warping and strandline deformation accompanying ice retreat. [After R. F. Flint (1957), *Glacial and Pleistocene Geology*, New York, John Wiley & Sons, p. 252, Figure 14.7.]

Wave action in this lake will produce a horizontal strandline. In *Phase 2* the ice front has receded some distance and the crust has risen, warping the first strandline so that it increases in elevation toward the north. In this phase a new horizontal strandline is formed at lake level. In *Phase 3* further ice recession has permitted additional crustal rise, upwarping the strandlines of both the first and second phases.

Figure 14.9 shows elevations of several warped strandlines of northeastern North America. These include marine shorelines as well as lakes. Notice that for Lake Ontario the present elevation of a single strandline is 400 ft (120 m) higher at the northeastern end than at the southwestern end. Degree of warping is less over the western Great Lakes. A dashed line shows the southern limit of warping, or *hinge-line,* which is approximately equivalent to the limit of Wisconsinan ice advance in the New England region.

In the Great Lakes region, several hinge-lines are recognized, as shown in Figure 14.9. These lines refer to lake levels in order of age from south to north. The oldest cuts across Lake Erie, while the youngest cuts across northern Lake Michigan.

Developmental history of the Great Lakes during recessional phases of the ice sheet is extremely complex. We make no attempt here to give a full sequence of events, but merely to pick out certain representative and interesting

points in time to illustrate the nature of the process. A series of maps in Figure 14.10 shows conditions at these selected points in time.

Map A shows conditions between −14,000 and −15,000 years in recessional phases of the Woodfordian Substage. Ice lobes in the basins of Lake Michigan and Lake Erie had receded sufficiently far to form two proglacial lakes, named *Chicago* and *Maumee,* respectively. The former drained south by means of the Desplaines River, and the latter drained into the Wabash River. Continued recession (*Map B*) enlarged these lakes, lowering the level of Lake Maumee and allowing it to drain west along the ice front into Lake Chicago. There followed an extensive ice recession interval not shown (Lake Arkona), followed by a readvance (Port Huron). At about −13,000 years the Erie basin was occupied by Lake Whittlesey (lower than its predecessor, Lake Maumee), which drained into *Lake Saginaw,* situated in what is now Saginaw Bay of Lake Huron (*Map C*). Lake Saginaw in turn drained into Lake Chicago. There followed a major ice recession, the Twocreekan interval, in which much of the area of the present lake basins was occupied by water and probably drained eastward into the St. Lawrence or Lake Champlain estuaries.

Again the ice advanced. This was the Valders advance of about −12,000 years, but it did not reach as far as previous advances. Conditions

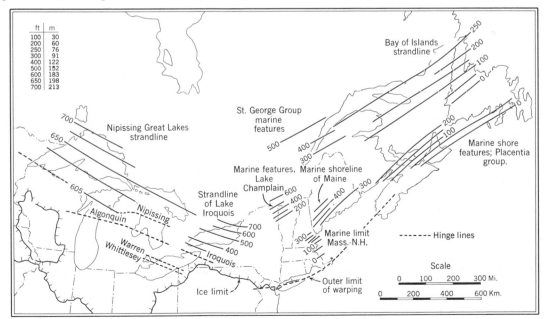

Figure 14.9. Altitudes of strandlines in eastern North America. Contours (isobases) are in units of feet above sea level. [Modified and simplified from a map by R. F. Flint (1957), *Glacial and Pleistocene Geology,* New York, John Wiley & Sons, p. 251, Figure 14.6. Hinge lines from J. L. Hough (1958), *Geology of the Great Lakes,* Urbana, Univ. of Illinois Press, p. 136, Figure 34.]

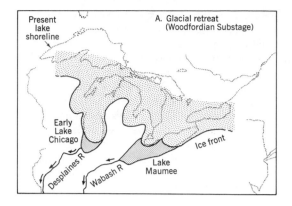

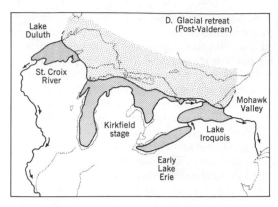

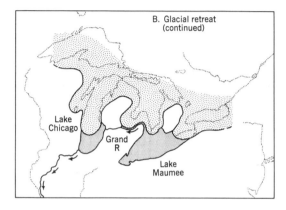

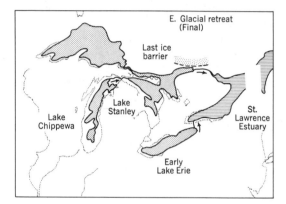

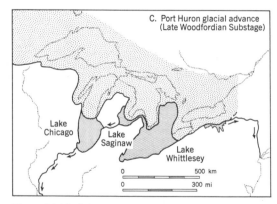

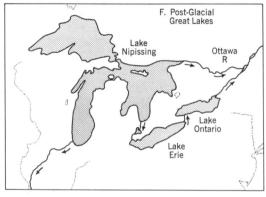

Figure 14.10. Selected stages in the development of the Great Lakes. [After J. L. Hough (1958), *Geology of the Great Lakes,* Urbana, Univ. of Illinois Press, pp. 284-296, Figures 54, 56, 60, 69, 73, and 74.)

shown in Map C were essentially resumed at the time of maximum Valders advance. Final recession of the ice front now was under way. *Map D* shows conditions later in Valderan time. Ice had receded from the western end of the Lake Superior basin, allowing the formation of *Lake Duluth,* which drained south by way of the St. Croix River. Lakes of the Michigan, Huron, Erie, and Ontario basins were now connected and drainage was eastward through the Mohawk Valley. Note that Huron drained directly into

Ontario by means of a channel along the ice front. At about −9000 years, or somewhat earlier, ice recession had opened a northern outlet channel from Georgian Bay of Lake Huron, allowing eastward drainage by way of Lake Nipissing and the Ottawa River into the St. Lawrence estuary (*Map E*).

The opening of this channel initiated an extremely low stage of lake levels, but this was reversed as crustal rebound raised the northern outlet. At about −4000 years, as shown in *Map*

F, lake levels had risen again, fusing the three upper lakes into one body (Lake Nipissing), which discharged simultaneously through three outlets—one into Lake Erie, a second by reoccupation of the Chicago outlet, and a third by way of the Ottawa River. Subsequently, because of increased crustal uplift in the north, the northern outlet by way of the Ottawa River was abandoned. Lake levels fell and the Chicago outlet was also abandoned.

F. CRUSTAL RISE FOLLOWING UNLOADING

The principle of isostasy, treated in Chapter 7 in *Planet Earth*, explains a remarkable phenomenon of Holocene time: the gradual rise of the earth's crust over areas formerly buried under glacial ice or submerged by water of large pluvial lakes. The nature of this crustal rise in the Great Lakes region has been described in Data Bank 14, section E. An even more striking example is that of the Baltic region, shown in Figure 14.11. Referring back to Figure 6.25 in *Planet Earth*, note that the center of the Scandinavian Ice Sheet was located over the Baltic Sea, spreading outward and thinning in all directions. Maximum

rate of postglacial rise coincides with the central region of greatest ice thickness.

Recall from Chapter 6 in *Planet Earth* that the crust beneath both the Greenland and Antarctic Ice Sheets is deeply depressed under existing ice load. After an ice sheet has disappeared, the process of isostatic adjustment sets in by the slow flowage of rock in the soft region of the mantle (asthenosphere) toward the depressed zone. Because the disappearance of ice was comparatively rapid, isostatic adjustment could not keep pace and the rise continues today.

Equally interesting is the crustal rise following the rapid shrinkage of pluvial Lake Bonneville. Figure 14.12 shows the present elevation of the highest shoreline of that lake. The central region has risen 70 ft (44 m). The maximum depth of Lake Bonneville was about 1000 ft (330 m), equal in load to a layer of rock 350 ft (105 m) thick. The lake would have depressed the crust by a much greater amount had it been in existence for a much longer span of time.

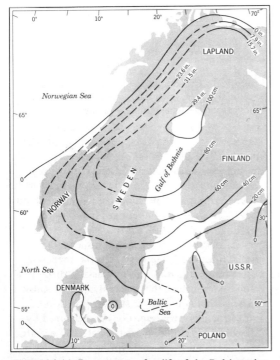

Figure 14.11. Present rate of uplift of the Baltic region is shown here by lines of equal uplift in centimeters per century, with equivalent values in inches per century. [Based on data by B. Gutenberg. After J. A. Jacobs, R. D. Russell, and J. T. Wilson (1959), *Physics and Geology*. New York, McGraw-Hill, p. 98, Figure 4.5.]

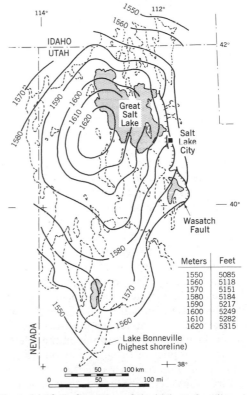

Meters	Feet
1550	5085
1560	5118
1570	5151
1580	5184
1590	5217
1600	5249
1610	5282
1620	5315

Figure 14.12. Deformation of the highest shoreline (dashed line) of Lake Bonneville, Utah, shown by elevation contours in meters. [After P. B. King (1965), in *The Quaternary of the United States*, H. E. Wright, Jr. and D. G. Frey, Eds., Princeton, N.J., Princeton Univ. Press, p. 850, Figure 14. Data of M. D. Crittenden, Jr., U.S. Geological Survey.]

BANK 15
THE CELESTIAL SPHERE

A. CELESTIAL COORDINATES

For purposes of astronomical description and navigation it is often convenient to revert to the Ptolemaic concept of a fixed earth about which the heavenly bodies revolve. That really is the impression any human being would receive from watching the sky hour after hour, day after day, and night after night. The "heavenly bodies" seem to be traveling upon the inside surface of an imaginary sphere, the *celestial sphere,* one-half of which we see at any given moment from an apparent vantage point at the center of the sphere. The other half is hidden beneath the horizon at all times, but can be inferred by the observation that sun, moon, and stars disappear below the horizon in the west, only to reappear above the horizon in the east some dozen or so hours later.

On the celestial sphere the sun, stars, and planets seem to be at an equal distance from us. Except for the moon these objects are so distant that the few thousands of miles of separation possible from two viewpoints on the earth's surface would make no perceptible difference in their position. The geometry required is there-fore that of a true sphere of very great radius with the earth occupying only the center point.

The division of the celestial sphere and the location of stars on it are carried out by means of great and small circles and the arcs of such circles, imagined to be drawn upon the celestial sphere in a replica of the grid of meridians and parallels used on the earth (see Data Bank 1).

First, the *celestial equator* is located as a great circle produced by extending, or *project-ing,* the earth's equator outward to the celestial sphere (Figure 15.1). Projections of the earth's axis serve to locate the *celestial poles. Polaris,* the polestar, lies very close to the north celestial pole on the celestial sphere. The position of a

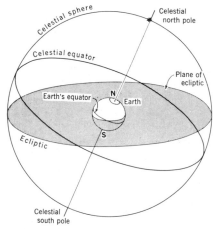

Figure 15.1. The celestial sphere projects the earth's equator and poles upon the inside of an imaginary spherical surface lying infinitely far away.

star north or south of the celestial equator is measured by its *declination,* which is the arc of an imaginary celestial meridian lying between the star and the celestial equator, just as for the latitude of a place on the earth's surface (Figure 15.2). Declination thus ranges from $0°$ to $90°$ north; from $0°$ to $90°$ south.

Analogous to the prime meridian as a ref-erence line is an imaginary celestial meridian, better named an *hour circle,* passing through a reference point on the celestial equator known as the *vernal equinox.* East-west position of a star (equivalent to longitude) is measured by *right ascension,* the arc of the celestial equator lying between the vernal equinox and the hour circle of the star (upper sphere in Figure 15.3). Unlike terrestrial longitude, with its $360°$ ($180°$ east, plus $180°$ west), right ascension is scaled in time units: hours, minutes, and seconds. Mea-surement is always eastward from the vernal equinox. There are 24 hr of arc for the entire

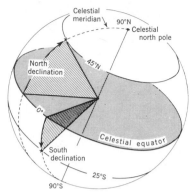

Figure 15.2. Declination on the celestial sphere is analogous to latitude on the earth.

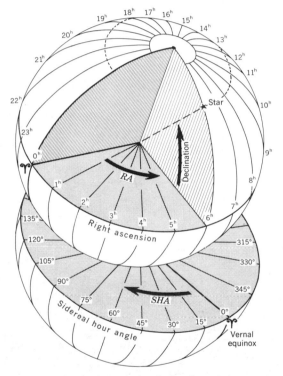

Figure 15.3. Right ascension of a star is analogous to the east longitude of a point on the earth. An alternative system, by sidereal hour angle, measures the angle in degrees in the westward direction, as in west longitude.

circumference, 1 hr being equivalent to 15 degrees of arc. Each degree of arc is equivalent to 4 min of time. Such a system has obvious disadvantages. Celestial angles are commonly measured with instruments scaled in degrees, minutes, and seconds of arc (not time). More recently, for navigational purposes, right ascension has been replaced by the *sidereal hour angle* (abbreviated to SHA), which is measured

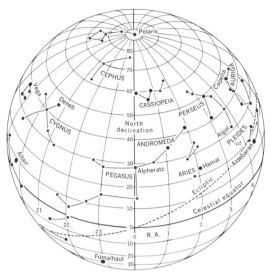

Figure 15.4. On the celestial globe, constellations are viewed as if from a point outside the celestial sphere. Compare with the star chart, Figure 15.5.

from 0° to 360° westward from the vernal equinox (lower portion of Figure 15.3). Thus, a right ascension of 6^h would be the same as 270° SHA.

B. CELESTIAL GLOBES AND MAPS

Just as the earth-grid and surface features of the earth may be shown on a true-scale earth model (the terrestrial globe), so it is possible to take a sphere and print on it the celestial hour circles of right ascension and the celestial parallels of declination (Figure 15.4). The major stars may then be located on the celestial globe and labeled, just as cities are on the terrestrial globe. It is important to remember that the celestial globe gives us an "outside," or external, view of the celestial relations. In order to see the constellations as they actually appear in the heavens, we would have to split open a transparent celestial sphere and examine the inner, concave surface or build a globe large enough for us to get inside and sit at the central point. (A large planetarium serves the same purpose.) The use of a globe of clear plastic permits us to look across the inside diameter to the other side and thus to see the constellations in their familiar configurations.

Just as there are many advantages in using a flat map of the earth, there are advantages in plotting the stars on a flat chart, termed a *star chart* (Figure 15.5). The star chart shown is based on a simple rectangular grid of equidistantly spaced lines, which greatly distorts both

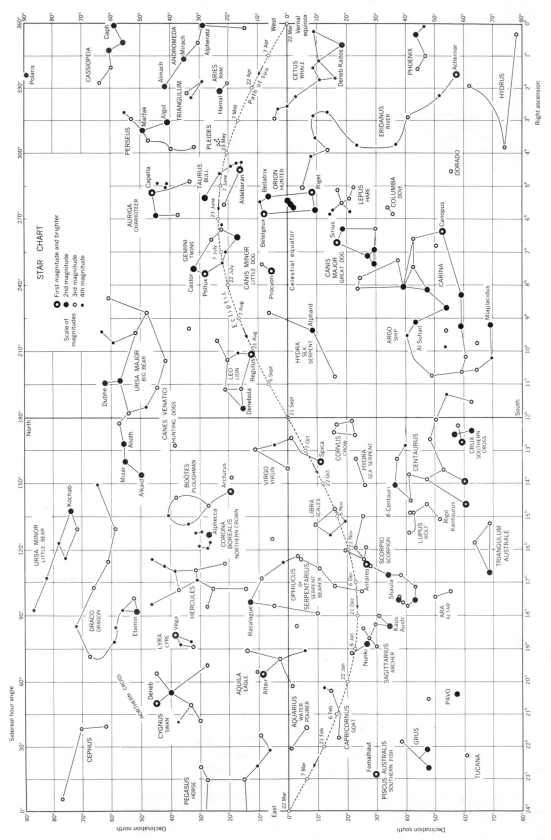

Figure 15.5. A star chart showing the principal stars and constellations. Dates on the ecliptic give the sun's position at intervals throughout the year. (Data from U.S. Navy Oceanographic Office Chart No. 2100.)

scales and areas, particularly in the higher dec- linations. The chart should be considered pri- marily as a graph, although near the celestial equator the shapes of constellations are quite well displayed. Note that east is toward the left on this chart. For a truer picture of constella- tions near the celestial poles, a type of map grid known as a polar projection should be used (see Data Bank 1, section B).

The stars (except for the sun) have fixed po- sitions in the celestial globe or chart; that is, their celestial coordinates are fixed. (For most purposes the changes in position due to aberra- tion of light and parallax may be disregarded.) Of course, as the earth turns, all the celestial objects seem to travel constantly from east to west, following the apparent daily rotation of the celestial sphere, but the stars do not move among themselves. On the other hand the sun, moon, and planets change their celestial coor- dinates slowly from hour to hour and from day to day, seeming to creep gradually from one constellation to another.

C. HORIZON SYSTEM OF CELESTIAL COORDINATES

Although the celestial sphere turns constantly, we can imagine, projected upon the celestial dome, a system of reference points and circles which are fixed with respect to our observation point on earth (Figure 15.6). The earth seems to be a flat, circular disk, bounded by the horizon. Projected upon the celestial sphere, our terres- trial horizon becomes the *celestial horizon*, a fixed great circle dividing the upper, or visible, hemisphere of the celestial sphere from the lower, or nonvisible, hemisphere. Directly above us, at the highest point of the celestial dome, is the *zenith*; directly below us, on the lowest point of the hidden celestial hemisphere, is the *nadir*. Passing directly overhead through the zenith and the celestial north and south poles is a fixed great circle, known simply as the *merid- ian*. It corresponds to an extension outward of the terrestrial meridian of the point on earth. The meridian intersects the horizon at points whose directions are the true geographic north and south. As the sun, moon, or a given star moves from east to west across the sky, it must cross the meridian. This event is termed the *meridian passage,* or *upper transit,* of the object. In the case of the sun the meridian passage is termed *apparent solar noon.*

The horizon system of reference points and circles permits us to describe the position of a celestial body at a given instant of time with reference to our position on earth (Figure 15.7). *Altitude* is the angular distance, in degrees, mea- sured upward from the horizon to the object along an imaginary great circle (referred to as a *vertical circle*) that would pass through the zenith point (angle *HCP* in Figure 15.7). Thus the altitude of an object in the sky can range from 0° at the horizon to 90° at zenith. Alti- tude below the horizon can also be stated as a negative angle, although the object cannot be seen.

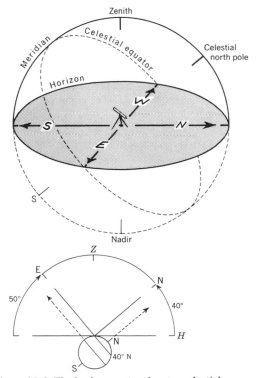

Figure 15.6. The horizon system locates celestial bodies on a hemispherical dome fixed with respect to the observer's horizon and zenith.

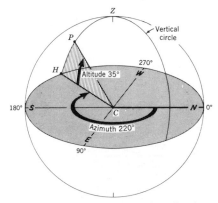

Figure 15.7. Azimuth and altitude describe the posi- tion of a star in terms of the horizon system of coordi- nates.

Azimuth is the horizontal direction of a line from the observer to that point where the vertical circle cuts the horizon (angle *NCH* in Figure 15.7). In navigation azimuth is measured with reference to true geographic north, beginning at the north point and going toward the east through a total of 360°. A point lying in the eastern half of the sky would have an azimuth in the range from 0° to 180°; a point in the western half of the sky would fall in the azimuth range 180° to 360°. Any other azimuth system could just as well be used, if desired.

To clarify the distinction between the celestial coordinates—declination and right ascension (or SHA)—and the horizon-system coordinates—altitude and azimuth—the following points may be helpful. The celestial coordinates are permanently located on the celestial sphere, so that the entire system appears to turn from east to west as the earth rotates, but the stars remain fixed in relation to the imaginary grid of hour circles and celestial parallels. In contrast, the altitude and azimuth of a star vary, not only with the latitude of the observer on the earth's surface, but also constantly with time. Therefore a statement of the celestial coordinates of a star holds valid, no matter where or when the star is observed, whereas a statement of the altitude and azimuth of a star is meaningless unless the position of the observer and the exact time of observation are also stated.

D. SIDEREAL TIME

It is common knowledge that the earth rotates on its axis at such a rate as to make one complete turn in a day of 24 hr. In astronomy and the earth sciences two definitions of the day must be considered, as well as two varieties of time. One complete turn of the earth on its axis constitutes the *period of rotation,* but we must define exactly what is meant by a complete turn. What reference point is used?

An absolute framework of reference is provided by the stars. One rotation of 360°, a full circle with respect to the stars, defines the *sidereal day,* which is divided into 24 hr of *sidereal time,* popularly called *star time* (Figure 15.3). We on the earth's surface feel no sensation of the earth turning under us; instead the entire celestial sphere seems to turn around us. Thus the sidereal day is the period of time required for a given star to return to the same position in the sky after one full rotation of the celestial sphere. Suppose that we should aim a telescope exactly upon the celestial meridian, noting the exact time by our watches at which a certain star crosses that meridian. The next meridian passage of that same star a night later will be found to occur about 4 min earlier than it did the first night. Our watches follow solar time, the system in daily use throughout the world of civil affairs. According to solar time the sidereal day amounts to about $23^h 56^m$.

Solar time, defined broadly, is time measured in reference to the sun's position. Figure 15.8 shows that a complete turn of the earth with respect to the sun is not the same as a complete turn with respect to the stars. The explanation lies in the fact that the earth is revolving in its orbit. This daily orbital motion is greatly exaggerated in Figure 15.8 to illustrate the principle. On a given day, with the earth located at point *A,* the sun at noon is assumed to be in direct line with a particular star so that the meridian passage of both occurs simultaneously. One sidereal day later, with the earth now at point *B,* the earth has rotated through 360°; therefore the same star is exactly over the meridian, but the sun and star are no longer in line. Instead

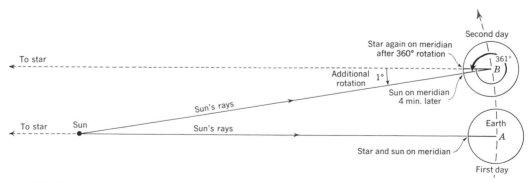

Figure 15.8. The solar day is about 4 minutes longer than the sidereal day. Angles are greatly exaggerated in this diagram.

the earth must turn about $1°$ more to bring the sun over the meridian. To turn this additional degree requires about 4 minutes of time, making the solar day that much longer than the sidereal day.

The following exact equivalents may be useful for reference:

$$24^h \text{ sidereal time} = 23^h56^m4.09^s \text{ mean solar time}$$

$$24^h \text{ mean solar time} = 24^h03^m56.555^s \text{ sidereal time}$$

$$\text{one sidereal day} = 86,400 \text{ sidereal seconds}$$
$$= 86,164 \text{ mean solar seconds}$$

$$\text{one mean solar day} = 86,400 \text{ mean solar seconds}$$
$$= 86,636\tfrac{1}{2} \text{ sidereal seconds.}$$

The observed solar day varies in length throughout the year. Hence a uniform standard of time based on the sun must take the mean length of a solar day for the entire year, a unit known as the *mean solar day*. Our clocks and watches are regulated to conform to the mean solar day, which is divided into exactly 24 hr of mean solar time.

INDEX

Absolute Celsius scale, 22
Acceleration of gravity, 16
Agonic line, 13
Air pressure, *see* Pressure,
    atmospheric
Air temperature, 20
    measurement, 20
    scales, 21
    world maps, 25
Albite, 58, 59, 60
Alkali feldspars, 59
Almandite, 60
Altitude, celestial, 111
    of sun, 8, 9
Altocumulus, 34
Altonian Substage, 102-103
Altostratus, 34
Alumina, 59
Aluminosilicates, 58
Aluminum ore, 74
Amphibole group, 58, 60, 64
Andalusite, 60
Andesine, 60
Anemometer, 23
Aneroid barometer, 22
Anhydrite, 56, 72
Animals, evolution, 94-97
Anorthite, 58, 60
Anorthosite, 68
Antarctic Circumpolar Current,
    31
Antarctic Ocean, currents, 30
Antarctica, temperatures, 27
Anticyclone, 40
Antimony ore, 75
Antipode, 2
Apatite, 57
Aphanitic texture, 66
Aphelion, 6, 8
Appalachian Orogeny, 98
Appalachians, 98
    geologic evolution, 98
Aragonite, 71
Arctic Ocean, currents, 29
Argentite, 76
Asbestos, 70
Astrogeodetic ellipsoid, 15
Atomic structure of minerals, 60

Augite, 58, 60, 64
Axis of earth, 2
Azimuth, 23
    celestial, 112
Azimuthal equal-area projection, 6

Badlands, 54
Balloons for weather observation,
    24
Baltic region, crustal rise, 107
Bar, 22
Barograph, 23
Barometer, 22
    aneroid, 22
    mercurial, 22
Barometric pressure, *see*
    Pressure, atmospheric
Basalt, 19
Basin area and discharge, 52
Basins, *see* Drainage basins
Batholith, 68
Bauxite, 56, 70, 74
Bearings, compass, 81
Bedding planes, 81
    dip and strike, 81
Benguela Current, 28
Bifurcation ratio, 49, 52
Biofacies, 94
Biostratigraphic units, 90
Biostratigraphy, 90-94
Biotite, 58, 59
Bog ore, 70
Bonding of crystals, 62
    covalent, 62
    ionic, 62
    metallic, 62
    van der Waal's, 62, 65
Bouguer anomaly, 17
Bouguer correction, 17
Bourdon tube, 21
Bowen reaction series, 70
Brazil Current, 28
Bright Angel formation, 90, 92
Bulk modulus, 87
Bytownite, 60

Calcite, 56, 57, 71
California Current, 28

Cambrian strata of Grand
    Canyon, 90, 92
Canadian Shield, 99
Canary Current, 28
Carbon dioxide, atmospheric, 101
Carbon-14, 101
    half-life, 101
Carbonate sediment, 93
Carbonates, 56
Carnotite, 75
Cassiterite, 75
Cavendish, 18
Celestial coordinates, 108-109
    horizon system, 111
Celestial equator, 108
Celestial horizon, 111
Celestial poles, 108
Celestial sphere, 8, 108
    on globe, 109
Celsius scale, 21
    absolute, 22
Cenozoic Era, 98-107
    in Appalachians, 98
Chalcocite, 75
Chalcopyrite, 75
Channel segments, 48
Chezy equation, 47
Chlorite, 70
Chromite, 74
Chromium ore, 74
Cinnabar, 76
Circle of illumination, 8, 9
Cirrocumulus, 34
Cirrostratus, 34
Cirrus, 34, 40
Clay minerals, 69, 70
Cleavage of minerals, 55, 60
    planes, 55
Clouds, 34-37
    classes, 34
    classification, 34
    cumuliform, 37
    in cyclonic storms, 40
    families, 34
    forms, 34
    on fronts, 40
    high, 34
    lenticular, 37

Clouds (*Continued*)
  low, 34
  middle, 34
  vertical, 34
Coastal Plain, 100
Cobalt ore, 75
Cobaltite, 75
Colatitude, 8
Cold pole, 25
Compass-quadrant bearings, 81
Conchoidal fracture, 56
Constant-ratio scale, 71
Constellations on star chart, 111
Continents, crustal structure, 88
Contour interval, 77
Contour line, 77
Contour maps, 77
  construction, 78
  reading, 78
  topographic, 77
Coordinates, celestial, 108-109
  geographic, 2
  horizon system, 111
Copper, native, 56, 75
Copper ores, 75
Cordilleran highlands, 98
Core of earth, 19, 86
  inner, 87
  properties, 87
Corundum, 57
Cosmic particles and radio-carbon
      dates, 101
Country rock, 68
Cretaceous Period in North
      America, 98-100
Crust of earth, 88
  continental, 88
  downwarping by ice, 104
  and earthquake waves, 88
  of ocean basins, 89
  thickness, 88
Crustal rebound, 106, 107
Crystal form of minerals, 55
  external, 55
Crystal lattice, 55
Crystal systems, 55
Cumulonimbus, 37
  equatorial, 39
Cumulus, 37, 40
  congested, 37
Current meter, 46
  Price type, 47
Currents, *see* Ocean currents
Cyclones, 40-45
  life cycle, 41

Dacite, 67
Datum, 77
Day, duration, 9
  mean solar, 113
  sidereal, 112, 113

Declination, celestial, 108
  magnetic, 11, 13
  maps, 13
  of sun, 8
Deserts, 25, 39-40
  arctic, 40
  middle-latitude, 39
  polar, 40
  tropical, 25, 39
Diamond, 55, 56
Diaspore, 70
Dikes, igneous, 68
Dinosaurs, evolution, 96
Dip of rock plane, 81
  symbols, 81
Discharge of stream, 47, 52
  and basin area, 52
Dolomite, 56, 71
Drainage basins, 48
  area law, 50, 52
  areas, 50
  and discharge, 52
  first-order, 50
  geometry, 48
Drainage density, 52
  controls, 52
  factors, 54
Drift of ocean water, 28
Dunite, 19, 68
Dyne, 22

Earth, density, 18, 19
  diameter, 14
  dimensions, 14, 15
  interior, 19
  mass, 18
  volume, 19
Earth coordinates, 1
Earth ellipsoids, 14-15
  Astrogeodetic, 15
  axes, 14
  Fischer, 15
  flattening, 14
  Geodetic Reference, 15
  International, 15
  Krasovskiy, 15
Earth-grid, 1
  projections, 3
Earth satellites, orbiting, 15
Earthquake waves, *see* Seismic
      waves
Earthquakes, recording, 82
Earth's figure, 14-15
  and gravity, 17
East, 2
East Australia Current, 28
East Greenland Current, 30
Ecliptic circle, 8
Elevations on map, 78
Ellipse of revolution, 14
Ellipsoid, oblate, 14

Energy, sensible, 20
Environments of sediment
      deposition, 93
Epeirogenic crustal rise, 98
Equator, 2
  celestial, 108
Equatorial Countercurrent, 27
Equinoxes, 7, 8
  autumnal, 8
  dates, 8
  vernal, 8
Evaporites, 73
Evolution, charts, 94-97

Faces of crystals, 55
Facies, 94
Fahrenheit scale, 21
Farmdalian Substage, 102-104
Faulting in Triassic Period, 98
Faults on geologic maps, 80
Faunal horizon, 90
Faunal zone, 90
Faunas, 90
Feldspars, 56
  alkali, 59
  atomic structure, 65
Feldspathoids, 59, 67
Ferric oxide, 73
Ferrous oxide, 73
Fiords, 40
Fischer ellipsoid, 15
Flume experiment, 47
Fluorite, 56, 57
Focus, of earthquake, 84
  of ellipse, 6
Fog, 28
Force, centripetal, 16
Formation, geologic, 90
Fossils, 90
  Cambrian, 90, 92
  of Grand Canyon, 90
Fractostratus, 36
Free-air correction of gravity, 17
Fronts on weather map, 40
  cold, 40
  occluded, 40
  warm, 40

Gal, 16
Galena, 56, 75
Galvanometer, 12
Gammas, 11
Garnet group, 60, 71
Geodetic Reference ellipsoid, 15
Geometric progression, 49
Geosynclines, 98
Glaciation, Wisconsinan, 102
Glass, volcanic, 66
Globes, celestial, 109
Glossopleura-Alokistocare
      faunal zone, 90

Gneiss, 61
Gold, 56, 76
Gold ores, 76
Gradient of isopleths, 77
Grand Canyon, 90
    biostratigraphy, 90
    formations, 90
    fossils, 90
    lithofacies, 94
Granite, 19, 67
    and seismic waves, 88
Granite-gabbro series, 67
Granodiorite, 67
Graphite, 60
Gravimeter, 16
    portable, 17
Gravitation, 18
    Newton's law, 18
    universal constant, 18
Gravity, 15-18
    acceleration, 16
    Bouguer correction, 17
    causes of variation, 16
    and centripetal force, 16
    field measurement, 17
    free-air correction, 17
    measurement, 16
    Potsdam standard, 16
    world standard, 16
Gravity anomaly, 17
Great circle, 1
Great Lakes, 104-107
    depths, 104
    developmental history,
        105-107
    elevations, 104
    hinge-line, 105
    surface areas, 104
    warped strandlines, 105
Greenland, temperatures, 27
Greenwich meridian, 3
Grid of earth coordinates, 1
    on projections, 3
Groundmass, 66
Gulf Stream, 27
Gypsum, 56, 57, 72
Gyre, 28

Hachured line, 78
Halides, 56
Halite, 56, 61, 73
Halo in clouds, 34
Hardness of minerals, 56
Hayford, J. F., 15
Heavy minerals, 71
Hematite, 56, 73, 74
Hexagonal system, 55, 57
High of barometric pressure, 40
Hinge-line, 105
Holocene Epoch, 103
    crustal rise, 107

Horizon system, 111
Hornblende, 58, 60, 64
Horton, R. E., 51
Horton's laws of streams, 51-52
Hour circle, 108
Hudson Valley region, 98
Humboldt Current, 28
Hurricane barograph trace, 23
Hydraulic radius, 47
Hydrolysis, 69
Hydroxides, 56
Hydroxyl ion, 59, 65
Hygrograph, recording, 34
Hygrometer, 34

Ice, as mineral, 56
Illite, 56, 70
Illumination circle, 8, 9
Ilmenite, 71, 74
Inclination, magnetic, 11
Inertia, 82
Intensity, magnetic, *see* Magnetic
        intensity
Interbasin areas, 50
International Astronomical
        Union, 15
International ellipsoid, 15, 17
International gravity formula, 17
International Union of Geodesy
        and Geophysics (IUGG),
        15
Intertonguing, 93
Invertebrates, evolution, 94
Ionic bonds, 62
Ionic groups, 62
Ions in crystal structure, 62
    atomic radius, 62
    charges, 63
    shared, 63
Iron in earth's core, 19
Iron ores, 74
Isarithm, 77
Isobar, 77
Isobath, 77
Isochron, 90
Isochronous surface, 90, 92
Isocline, 77
Isodyne, 77
Isogone, 77
Isogonic line, 77
Isogonic map, 13
Isohyet, 39, 77
Isohypse, 77
Isometric system, 55, 57, 62
Isopach, 77
Isopleth maps, 77
Isopleths, 77
Isostasy, 107
Isostatic uplift, 107
    in Appalachians, 98
    in Baltic region, 107

    in Great Lakes
    in Holocene time, 107
Isotach, 77
Isotherms, 24, 25, 77
    of air temperature, 25
    of sea surface, 24
    on weather map, 40

Jointing, 68
    columnar, 68
Jurassic Period, 98

Kaolinite, 56, 69
Kelvin scale, 22
Knot, 15
Krasovskiy ellipsoid, 15
Kuroshio Current, 27
Kyanite, 60

Labrador Current, 30
Labradorite, 60
Laccolith, 68
Lake Bonneville, 107
    crustal rise, 107
Lake Chicago, 105
Lake Duluth, 106
Lake Erie, 104
Lake Huron, 104
Lake Maumee, 105
Lake Michigan, 104
Lake Nipissing, 106, 107
Lake Ontario, 104
Lake Saginaw, 105
Lake Superior, 104
Lake Whittlessey, 105
Laramian orogeny, 101
Latite, 67
Latitude, 1, 2
    lengths of degrees, 15
Lavas, 67
Laws of stream systems, 49-52
    basin areas, 50
    equations, 51-52
    of Horton, 51
    lengths, 50
    numbers, 49
    slopes, 51
Lead ore, 75
Leap year, 7, 8
Length ratio of streams, 50, 52
Libby, W. F., 101
Lightning, 37
Limonite, 56, 70, 74
Lithofacies, 94
Lithologic units, 90
Logarithmic scale, 49, 71
Longitude, 1, 2
    length of degree, 15
Love waves, 86
Loxodrome, 5

Mackerel sky, 34
Magnesium ore, 74
Magnetic elements, 11
    measurement, 11
Magnetic field of earth, 101
Magnetic intensity, 11
    charts, 11
    horizontal, 11
    maps, 11
    total, 11
    vertical, 11
Magnetic observatories, 13
Magnetism of earth, 11-13
Magnetite, 71, 74
Magnetogram, 13
Magnetograph, 13
Magnetometer, 11
    airborne, 12
    deflection, 11
    oscillation, 11
    portable, 12
    proton vector, 12
Mammals, evolution, 96
Manganese ores, 74
Manganite, 74
Manning equation, 48
Mantle of earth, 86, 87
Map projections, 3-6
    azimuthal equal-area, 6
    conformal, 3
    equal-area, 3, 5, 6
    equatorial, 3
    interrupted, 6
    Mercator, 4
    oblique, 3
    polar, 3
    recommended, 6
    sinusoidal, 5
    stereographic, 3
    tilted, 3
Map scale, 78
    on projections, 4
Maps, 3, 77-81
    areal, 80
    celestial, 109
    contour, 77
    geologic, 80
    isopleth, 77
    isothermal, 24, 25
    paleogeographic, 94, 98
    scales, 78
    topographic, 77
    weather, 4
Mares' tails, 34
Mass, 18
    of earth, 18
M-discontinuity, 89
Mercator, Gerardus, 4
Mercator projection, 4
Mercury Datum, 15
Mercury ore, 76

Meridian arc, 14
Meridian of Greenwich, 3
Meridian passage, 111
Meridians, 1, 2
    celestial, 108, 111
    prime, 2
    properties, 2
Metals, ore, 74-76
Meter, international, 15
Mica group, 55, 58, 59
    alteration, 69
    atomic structure, 64
Microcline, 58, 69
    alteration, 69
Mile, 15
    international nautical, 15
    nautical, 15
    statute, 15
Millibar, 22
Milligal, 16
Mineral alteration, 69-71
Mineral varieties (species),
        albite, 58, 59, 60
    almandite, 60
    amphibole group, 58, 60, 64
    andalusite, 60
    andesine, 60
    anhydrite, 56, 72
    anorthite, 58, 60
    apatite, 57
    aragonite, 71
    argentite, 76
    asbestos, 70
    augite, 58, 60, 64
    bauxite, 56, 70, 74
    biotite, 58, 59
    bytownite, 60
    calcite, 56, 57, 71
    carnotite, 75
    cassiterite, 75
    chalcocite, 75
    chalcopyrite, 75
    chlorite, 70
    chromite, 74
    cinnabar, 76
    cobaltite, 75
    copper, native, 56, 75
    corundum, 57
    diamond, 55, 56
    diaspore, 70
    dolomite, 56, 71
    feldspars, 56, 59, 65, 69
    feldspathoids, 67
    fluorite, 56, 57
    galena, 56, 75
    garnet group, 60, 71
    gold, native, 56, 76
    graphite, 60
    gypsum, 56, 57, 72
    halite, 56, 61, 73
    hematite, 56, 73, 74

    hornblende, 58, 60, 64
    ice, 56
    illite, 56, 70
    ilmenite, 71, 74
    kaolinite, 56, 69
    kyanite, 60
    labradorite, 60
    limonite, 56, 70, 74
    magnetite, 71, 74
    manganite, 74
    mica group, 55, 58, 59, 64
    microcline, 58, 69
    molybdenite, 75
    montmorillonite, 70
    muscovite, 58, 60, 69
    nepheline, 59, 67
    oligoclase, 60
    olivine, 19, 56, 58, 60, 63
    orthoclase, 56, 57, 58
    pentlandite, 74
    pitchblende, 75
    plagioclase, 58, 69
    platinum, 76
    potash feldspar, 58, 69
    pyrite, 74
    pyrolusite, 74
    pyroxene group, 58, 60, 64
    quartz, 55, 56, 57, 63
    rutile, 74
    serpentine, 70
    silver, native, 76
    sphalerite, 56, 75
    staurolite, 60
    stibnite, 75
    sulfur, native, 56
    talc, 57, 70
    topaz, 57
    tremolite, 60
    uraninite, 75
    wolframite, 75
    wollastonite, 60
    zircon, 71
Minerals, 55-66, 69-76
    alteration, 69
    atomic structure, 56, 60
    biogenic, 71
    chemical groups, 55
    clay, 69
    cleavage, 55
    color, 57
    composition, 55
    crystal form, 55
    detrital, 71
    evaporite, 73
    feldspathoid, 67
    fracture, 56
    heavy, 71
    hydrogenic, 71
    luster, 57
    optical properties, 57
    ores, 74-76

Minerals (*Continued*)
   physical properties, 55
   relative density, 56
   in sediments, 69
   specific gravity, 56
   streak, 57
Moho, 89
Mohorovičić discontinuity, 89
Mohs scale, 57
Moisture, atmospheric, 34
Molybdenite, 75
Molybdenum ore, 75
Monoclinic system, 57
Montmorillonite, 70
Moraines, recessional, 103
Mountain waves, 37
Muav formation, 91
Muscovite, 58, 60
   alteration, 69

Nadir, 111
National Ocean Survey, 11, 13
National Oceanic and Atmospheric
     Administration (NOAA),
     4, 11
National Weather Service, 4, 40
Native elements, 56
Native gold, 76
Native silver, 76
Nepheline, 59, 67
Nepheline syenite, 68
Net radiometer, 20
Nevadian Orogeny, 98
Nickel ore, 74
Night, duration, 9
Nimbostratus, 36, 40
Nimbus, 36, 37
Noon, apparent solar, 111
   solar, 8
North, geographic, 2
North America in Cretaceous time,
   98
North Atlantic drift, 29
North Equatorial Current, 27
Norway Current, 29

Obsidian, 66
Ocean currents, 27-31
   equatorial, 27
   world patterns, 27
Ocean surface temperatures, 24
   annual range, 25
   maps, 24
Oersted, 11
Oligoclase, 60
Olivine, 19, 56, 58, 60
   atomic structure, 63
Orbit of earth, 6
   dimensions, 6
   and seasons, 8
Orders of stream segments, 48

Ore minerals, 74-76
Orogeny, in Appalachians, 98
   in Rocky Mountains, 101
Orthoclase, 56, 57, 58
Orthorhombic system, 57
Outcrops on maps, 81
Oxides, 56
   of iron, 73
     ferric, 73
     ferrous, 73

Paleogeographic map, 94
Paleozoic Era, 98
Parallels, 1, 2
   properties, 2
Peat of interglacial substage, 103
Pegmatite, 66, 68
Pendulum and gravity, 16
   and earth mass, 18
Peneplain, in Appalachians, 98
   of Canadian shield, 100
Pentlandite, 74
Perihelion, 6, 8
Peru Current, 28
Petrography, 66
Phaneritic texture, 66
Phenocrysts, 66
Phi scale, 71
Phonolite, 68
Pilot balloons, 24
Pitchblende, 75
Plagioclase feldspars, 58
   alkalic, 58
   alteration, 69
   calcic, 58
   sodic, 58
Plants, evolution, 95
   vascular, 95
Platinum, 76
Platinum ore, 76
Playfair's law, 51
Plutons, 68
Polaris, 108
Poles, 2
   celestial, 108
   geographic, 2
Polestar, 108
Porphyry, 66
Potash feldspar, 58, 69
Poynting balance, 18
Precipitation, 37-40
   annual, 38
   in cyclonic storm, 40
   equatorial, 39
   global pattern, 39
   intensity, 38
   measurement, 37
   monthly, 38
   subtropical, 40
   of west coasts, 40
   world types, 38

Pressure, atmospheric, 22
   measurement, 22-23
   sea-level, 22
   standard value, 22
   units, 22
   world maps, 27
Primary waves (P-waves), 84-87
Primates, evolution, 97
Prime meridian, 2
Profile, topographic, 78
Proglacial lake, 104
Projections, *see* Map projections
Psychrometer, 34
Pumice, 66
P-waves, 84-87
Pyranometer, 20
Pyrheliometer, 20, 21
Pyrite, 74
Pyrolusite, 74
Pyroxene group, 58, 60, 64
Pyroxenite, 68

Quartz, 55, 56, 57
   lattice structure, 63
Quartz latite, 67
Quartz syenite, 67

Radar weather observation, 24
Radiation, instruments, 20
   measurement, 20
   shortwave, 20
Radiocarbon age determination,
   101
Radiocarbon dates, 101
   discrepancies, 101
   and magnetic field, 101
Radiometer, 20
Radiosonde, 24
Rain gauge, 38
Rain shadow, 40
Rainfall, 39-40
   of equatorial belt, 39
   orographic, 39
Rating curve, 47
Rawinsonde, 24
Rayleigh waves, 86
Refraction of seismic waves, 88
Regression of strata, 93
Representative fraction, 78
Reptiles, evolution, 95
Revolution of earth, 6
   period, 6
   velocity, 6
Rhombs of calcite, 55, 71
Rhumb line, 5
Right ascension, 108
Rigidity of rock, 87
Rock salt, 56, 61
Rocks, igneous, 66-68
   aphanitic, 66
   classification, 66, 67

Rocks (*Continued*)
  composition, 67
  extrusive, 66
  fabric, 66
  felsic, 67
  granite-gabbro series, 67
  intrusive, 67, 68
  jointing, 68
  mafic, 67
  monomineralic, 68
  obsidian, 66
  phaneritic, 66
  plutonic, 67, 68
  pumice, 66
  textures, 66
  ultramafic, 68
  volcanic, 66
Rocky Mountain Geosyncline, 98
Rocky Mountain Seaway, 98
Rocky Mountains, 101
Roof pendant, 68
Rotation of earth, and gravity, 16
  period, 112
Rutile, 74

Sangamonian Stage, 103
Scale of map, 78
  fractional, 78
  graphic, 79
Scandinavian Ice Sheet, 107
Schist, 61
Scoria, 66
Scud, 36
Sea-surface temperatures, 24
  annual range, 25
  maps, 24
Sea water, freezing point, 25
Seasons, 8
  astronomical, 8
  duration, 8
Secondary waves (S-waves), 84
Seconds, mean solar, 113
  sidereal, 113
Sediments, minerals, 69
  size grades, 71
Seismic waves, 84-89
  amplitude, 82
  and core, 86
  and crustal structure, 88
  frequency, 82
  longitudinal, 85
  man-made, 88
  and mantle, 86
  and M-discontinuity, 89
  and Moho, 89
  nature, 85
  paths, 84
  primary, 84, 85
  recording, 82
  refraction, 88
  and rock rigidity, 87

  and rock type, 87
  secondary, 84, 85
  shadow zone, 86
  surface, 84
  transverse, 85
  travel-time curves, 85
Seismogram, 83, 84
  interpretation, 84
  sample, 84
Seismograph, 82-84
  construction, 83
  principle, 82
Semilogarithmic plot, 49
Semimajor axis, 14
Semiminor axis, 14
Serpentine, 70
Shadow zone, 86
Shear modulus, 87
Sidereal day, 112, 113
Sidereal hour angle (SHA),
  109, 112
Sidereal time, 112-113
Sieves for sediment, 71
Silica, 59
Silicate minerals, 57
  alteration products, 69
Silicates, 56
  hydrous, 56
Silcon-oxygen tetrahedron, 62
Sill, 68
Silver ores, 76
Sine curves, 5
Sine galvanometer, 12
Sinusoidal projection, 5
  interrupted, 6
Sling psychrometer, 34
Slope ratio, 51, 52
Small circle, 1
Snow measurement, 38
Solar beam, 20
Solar time, 112, 113
Solstice, 8
  dates, 8
  summer, 8, 10
  winter, 8, 9
South Equatorial Current, 27
Southern Ocean, currents, 30
Space lattice, 62
  cubic, 62
Specific gravity of minerals, 56
Sphalerite, 56, 75
Staff gauge, 46
Stage-discharge curve, 47
Stage of streams, 46
Star chart, 109
Star time, 112
Stationary wave, 37
Staurolite, 60
Steppes, 39
Stereographic projection, 3
Stibnite, 75

Stilling tower, 46
Stilling well, 46
Stock of igneous rock, 68
Storm track, 40
Storms, cyclonic, 40-45
  on weather map, 40
Strandlines of Great Lakes, 105
  warping, 105
Strata, carbonate, 92
  correlation, 90
Stratigrapher, 90
Stratigraphic column, 90
Stratigraphy, Pleistocene, 102
Stratocumulus, 36
Stratus, 36, 40
Streak of minerals, 57
Stream channels, 48
  density, 52
  fingertip, 48
  first-order, 48
  junctions, 48
  networks, 48
  orders, 48
  second-order, 48
  segments, 48
  slopes, 51
  third-order, 48
Stream discharge, 47, 52
  and basin area, 52
Stream gauging, 46
Stream length, 48, 52
  cumulative, 49, 52
  law, 50, 52
  mean, 49, 52
Stream networks, 48-52
  analysis, 49
  geometry, 48
  laws, 48-52
  slope analysis, 51
Stream numbers, law, 49, 52
Stream slope (gradient), 51
  law, 51, 52
Stream systems, 46-54
Stream velocity, 47
  and depth, 47
  and gradient, 47
  and hydraulic radius, 47
  mean, 47
  and slope, 47
Streams, 46-54
  depth, 47
  discharge, 47
  gauging, 46
  velocity, 47
Strike of rock plane, 81
Structure section, geologic, 81
Substages of Wisconsinan, 102
Sulfates, 56
Sulfides, 56
Sulfur, native, 56
Sun, declination, 8

Sun (*Continued*)
noon altitude, 8
Surface waves, 84
S-waves, 84-87
Syenite, 67, 68

Talc, 57, 70
Temperature, of air, *see*
Air temperature
atmospheric, *see* Air
temperature
and energy, 20
scales, 21
of sea surface, 24-25
Tetragonal system, 57
Tetrahedra, silicon-oxygen, 62
chains, 64
sheets, 64
Texture of igneous rock, 66
aphanitic, 66
equigranular, 66
phaneritic, 66
porphyritic, 66
scoriaceous, 66
Texture of stream channels, 53
coarse, 53
fine, 54
and rock type, 53
ultrafine, 54
Theodolite, 24
Thermocouple, 21
Thermometers, 20-22, 34
bimetallic, 20
compound-metal, 20
dry-bulb, 34
electrical resistance, 21
liquid-in-glass, 20
maximum-minimum, 20
in psychrometer, 34
wet-bulb, 34
Thunderhead, 37
Thunderstorms, 37
on fronts, 40
Tills of Wisconsinan Stage, 102

Time, mean solar, 7
sidereal, 112-113
solar, 112-113
Time-latitude diagram, 102
Time line, 90
Time units of strata, 92
Tin ore, 75
Titanium ores, 74
Tonalite, 67
Tongue, stratigraphic, 92, 93
Topaz, 57
Topographic depression, 78
Topography, 77
Torricelli, 22
Torsion balance, 18
Trachyte, 67
Trade-wind coasts, 39
Transgression of strata, 93
Transit, upper, 111
Travel-time curves, 85
Tremolite, 60
Triassic Period, 98
Triclinic system, 57
Trilobite, 90
Tropic of Cancer, 10
Tropic of Capricorn, 9
Tungsten ore, 75
Two Creeks ice advance, 101, 103
forest bed, 103
Twocreekan Substage, 102-104

Upwelling, 25, 28
Uraninite, 75
Uranium ore, 75
U.S. Geological Survey, 46

Valderan Substage, 102-104
in Great Lakes, 105
Van der Waal's bonding, 62, 65
Vanadium ore, 74
Vector quantity, 11
Veins, 68
Vernal equinox, 7, 8, 108
Vertical circle, 111
Volcanic ash, alteration, 70

Water-supply papers, 46
Water vapor, 34
measurement, 34
Wave, upper-air, 41
Wave cloud, 37
Wave cyclones, 40-45
Wave trough, upper-air, 41
Weather charts, upper-air, 41
Weather maps, 40-45
wind symbols, 24
Weather observations, 20-24
Wentworth scale, 71
West, 2
West-wind drift, 28
Wind-shift line, 40
Wind vane, 23
Winds, in cyclonic storms, 40
direction, 23
map symbols, 24
measurement, 23, 24
prevailing, 27
speed, 23, 24
velocity, 23
world maps, 27
Windward tropical coasts, 39
Wisconsinan Glaciation, 102
Wisconsinan Stage, 102-104
in middle-west, 102
Wolframite, 75
Wollastonite, 60
Woodfordian Substage, 102-104
and Great Lakes, 105

Year, 6, 7, 8
anomalistic, 8
sidereal, 8
tropical, 7, 8

Zenith, 8, 111
Zero, absolute, 22
Zinc, ore, 75
Zircon, 71
Zone, stratigraphic, 90
faunal, 90

72 73 74 75 76   9 8 7 6 5 4 3 2 1